rockschool®

Hot Rock
Drums Grade 5

8 classic rock tracks specially edited for Grade 5
for use in Rockschool examinations

www.rockschool.co.uk

Acknowledgements

Published by Rockschool Ltd. © 2014 under license from Music Sales Ltd
Catalogue Number RSK041410
ISBN: 978-1-908920-49-2

AUDIO
Produced by Tom Farncombe, Music Sales Ltd
Engineered, mixed and mastered by Jonas Persson, Music Sales Ltd

MUSICIANS
Arthur Dick, Noam Lederman, Paul Townsend, The Fullfat Horns

PUBLISHING
Compiled and edited by Noam Lederman, James Uings, Simon Pitt, Simon Troup and Jeremy Ward
Layout, internal design and music engraving by Simon and Jennie Troup, Digital Music Art
Cover designed by Philip Millard, Philip Millard Design
Additional proofing by Miguel Andrews
Audio and photographic copyright notices can be found at the back of the book

PRINTING
Printed and bound in the United Kingdom by Caligraving Ltd
Media hosting by Dropcards Inc

DISTRIBUTION
Exclusive Distributors: Music Sales Ltd

CONTACTING ROCKSCHOOL
www.rockschool.co.uk
Telephone: +44 (0)845 460 4747
Fax: +44 (0)845 460 1960

Table of Contents

Introductions & Information

Page

Rockschool Grade Pieces

Page

Additional Information

Page

Welcome to Hot Rock Drums Grade 5

Welcome to Hot Rock Drums Grade 5. This book of classic and contemporary tracks has been compiled to give you a resource to help you develop your drums and performance skills.

Songs

Hot Rock Drums Grade 5 contains eight songs that cover a wide range of styles and artists of the last 40 years. The songs can be used as Free Choice Pieces in the Rockschool Drums Grade 5 exam – see page 48 for more information on the preparing for and entering Rockschool exams. The songs can also be used in the performance units in public exams such as GCSEs. You can also enjoy playing them for their own sake, broadening your repertoire and learning many popular riffs and chord sequences in the process.

The songs in this book are arrangements of the original songs. While adjustments have been made to make the pieces playable at Grade 5 and to make them appropriate as examination pieces, we have worked hard to maintain the integrity and spirit of the original music.

Each song is printed over 2 to 4 pages and is preceded by a Fact File detailing information about the song, the band and the drummer who played on it and some recommended listening if you wish to research the artist further. At the end of each chapter there is a Walkthrough which gives you tips on how to play the piece and any technical challenges to look out for as you practise the song.

Audio

Each song in Hot Rock Drums has three audio tracks that can be downloaded via the download card that comes with the book. The first is a full track that includes the drum part and a full band. The other is a backing track with the drums taken off so you can play along with the band. The final track includes a click. The backing tracks should be used in examinations.

The audio files are supplied in mp3 format, the most widely compatible audio format in common usage – mp3s will likely be familiar to anyone with a computer, iPod, smartphone or similar device. Once downloaded you will be able to play them on any compatible device; we hope that you find this extra versatility useful.

Download Cards

Download cards are easy to use, simply go to *www.dropcards.com/hotrock* and type in the code on the back of your card. It's best to do this where you have a good connection so the download is uninterrupted. If for any reason you have a problem with your download please contact *www.dropcards.com/help* who will resolve any issues you may have.

Please note that most tablets and smartphones (including the iPad, iPhone and many Android-based devices) do not allow files to be downloaded directly on to the device. On the iPad and iPhone, files need to be downloaded to the Mac or PC first, then synced to the device using the iTunes application. Operating systems for mobile devices are updated frequently, so ensure you consult the most recent documentation available for your device and operating system for further details.

We hope that you enjoy playing these pieces. You can find further details about Rockschool's drums and other instrumental syllabuses by visiting our website at *www.rockschool.co.uk*.

The Smashing Pumpkins

SONG TITLE: CHERUB ROCK
ALBUM: SIAMESE DREAM
RELEASED: 1993
LABEL: VIRGIN
GENRE: ALTERNATIVE ROCK

PERSONNEL: BILLY CORGAN (VOX+GTR)
JAMES IHA (GTR)
D'ARCY WRETZKY (BASS)
JIMMY CHAMBERLIN (DRUMS)

UK CHART PEAK: 31
US CHART PEAK: N/A

BACKGROUND INFO

'Cherub Rock' is the first single off the Smashing Pumpkins' breakthrough second album *Siamese Dream*. The song begins with a set of mock marching band drum rolls before ploughing headlong into a straight-up hard rock assault. The drums were recorded (after many takes) by Jimmy Chamberlin.

THE BIGGER PICTURE

Siamese Dream had a troubled gestation. The Pumpkins had been signed to Virgin Records at the time of the grunge explosion and the band was being hotly touted as the 'next Nirvana'. The strain on the band members was intense with Corgan often re-recording the other members' parts, locking himself into the control room for hours at a time and sleeping in the studio.

Jimmy Chamberlin was experiencing acute personal problems and would go missing for days on end. Iha and Wretzky finished their romantic relationship. In the end, the record took eighteen months to record and came in at more than $250,000 over budget. However, *Siamese Dream* went on to sell more than 10 million copies worldwide, four million in the US alone.

NOTES

The first meeting between the self-taught, jazz-influenced Chamberlin and Billy Corgan was not promising: the drummer thought the band sounded terrible (they used a drum machine) while Corgan fretted about the drummer's mullet and yellow drum kit. But Chamberlin proved his worth by learning the band's songs after only one run through. He also persuaded Corgan to try harder material and on *Siamese Dream* the success of the formula became readily apparent. He remained the drummer for the next record but was sacked in 1996 for going AWOL once too often. He rejoined the Pumpkins when Corgan restarted the band in 2005 but left once again in 2009.

RECOMMENDED LISTENING

The Smashing Pumpkins debut record *Gish* (1991) contains the singles 'I Am One', 'Rhinoceros' and 'Siva'. This was followed by *Siamese Dream* (1993) which contains Pumpkins' classics such as 'Today', 'Disarm' and 'Rocket'. Its follow up, the two hour double album *Mellon Collie and the Infinite Sadness* (1995) was equally successful and spawned hits such as 'Bullet with Butterfly Wings', '1979', 'Zero' and the majestic 'Tonight'.

Cherub Rock

The Smashing Pumpkins

Words & Music by Billy Corgan

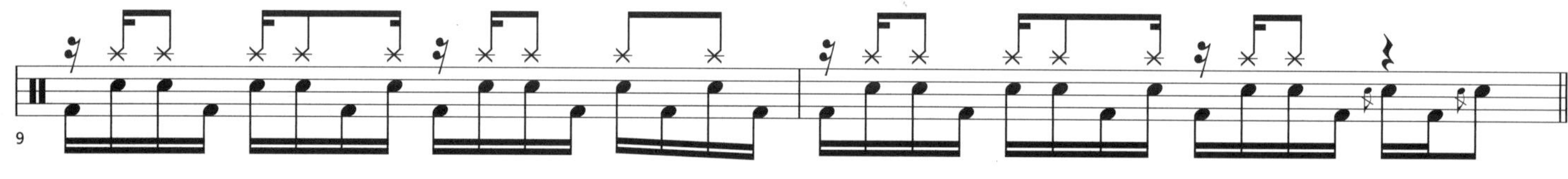

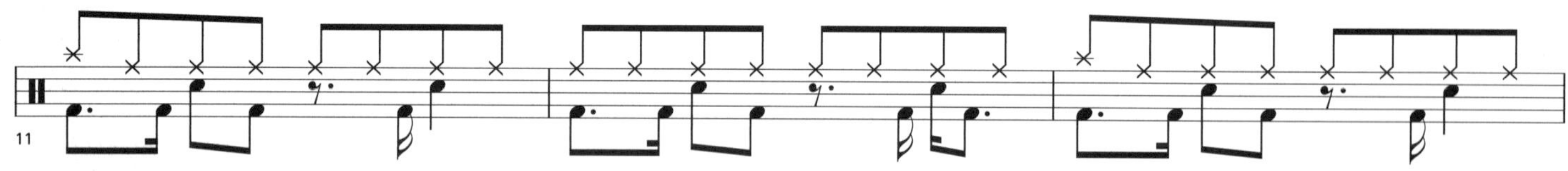

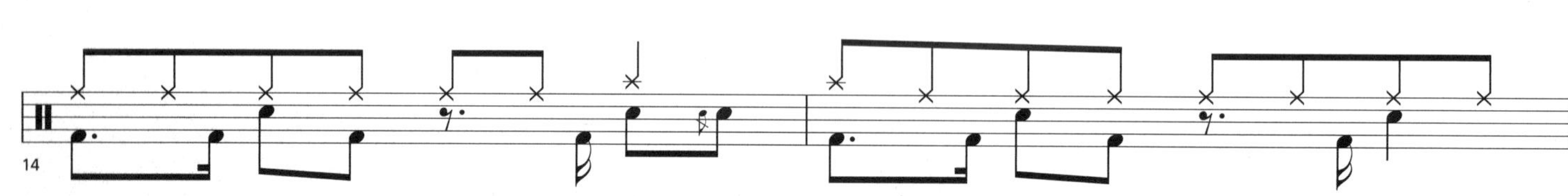

16

18

20

22

24

26

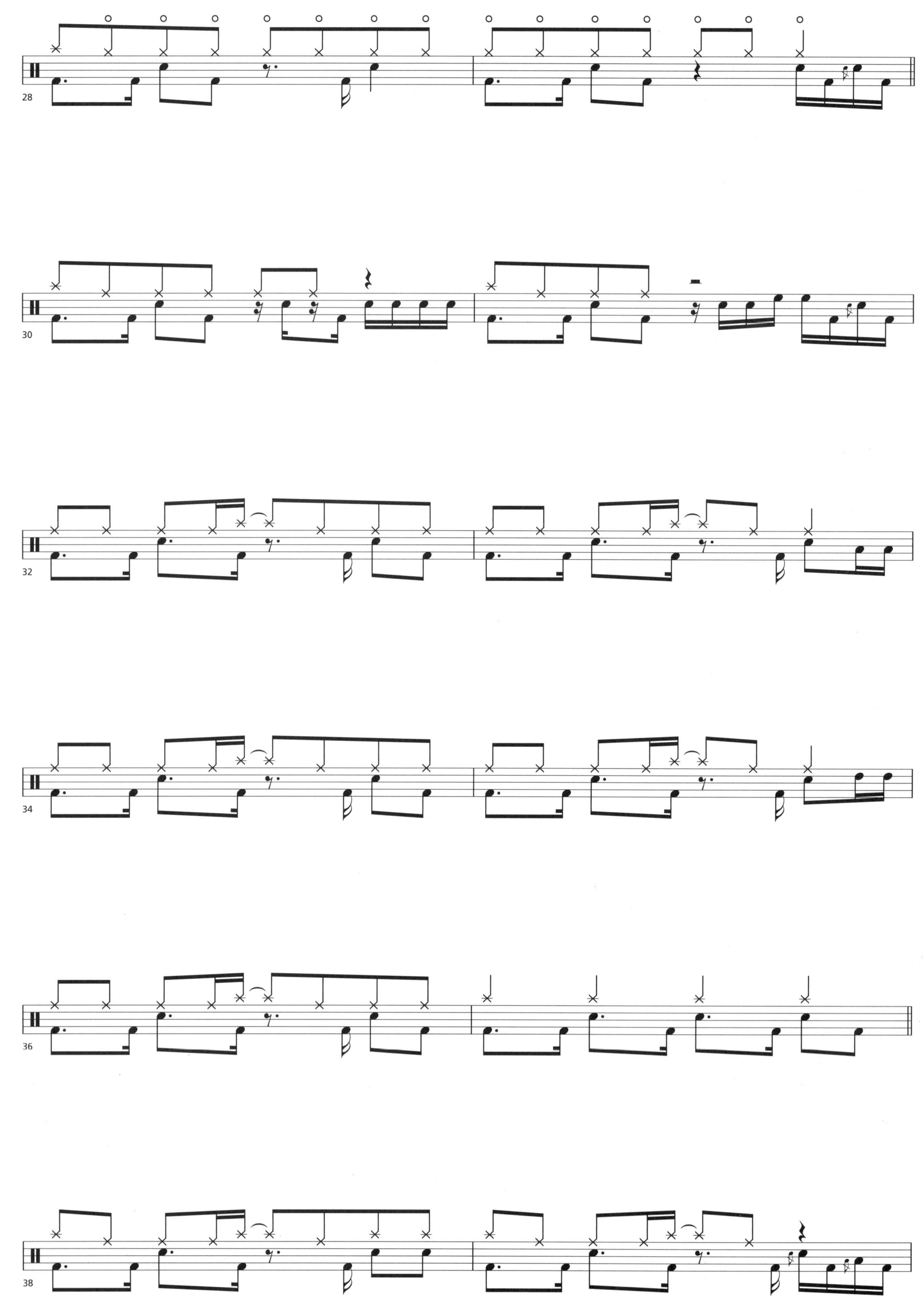
28
30
32
34
36
38

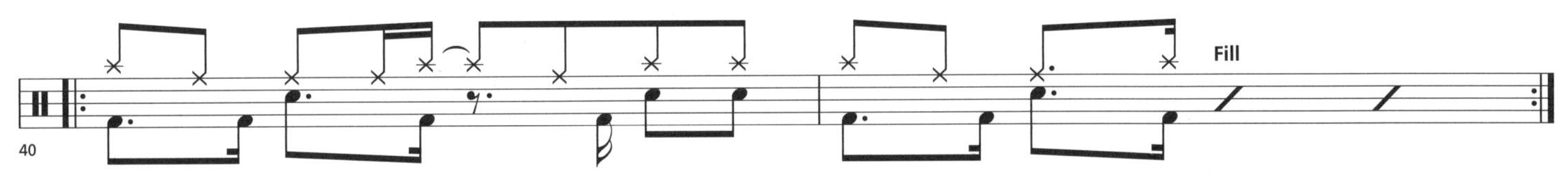
Fill
40

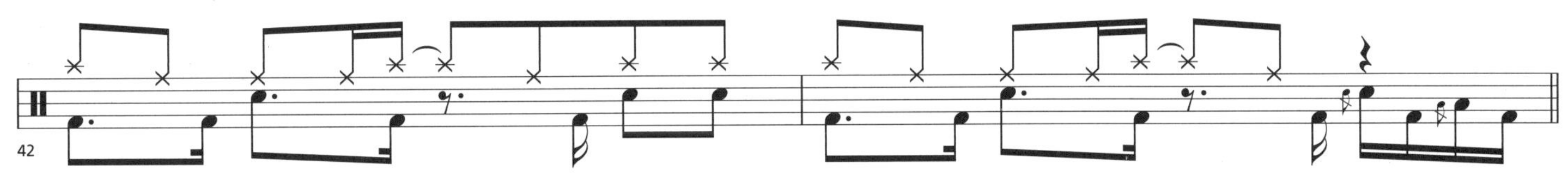
42

Solo (4 bars)
44

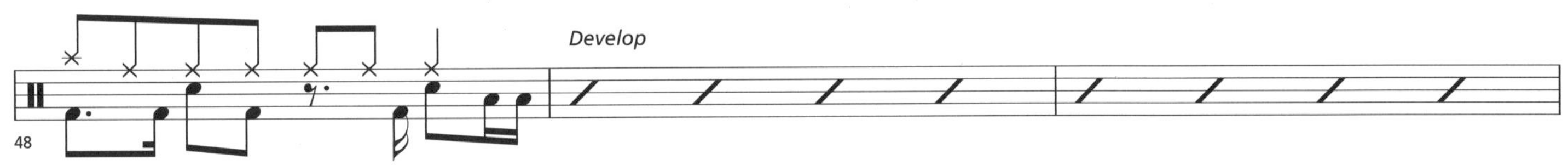
Develop
48

51

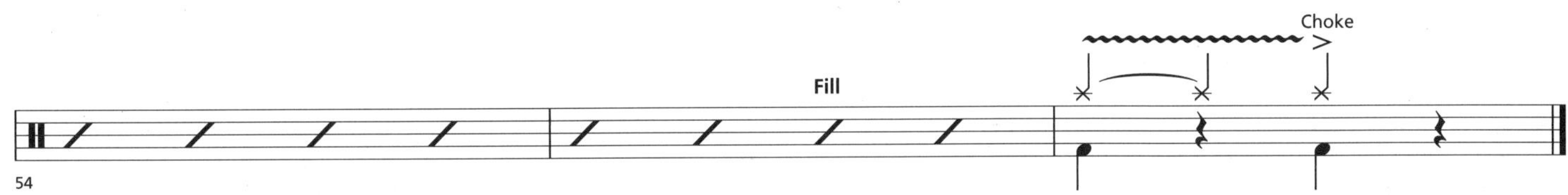
Choke
Fill
54

Walkthrough

Intro riff (Bars 1–10)

After the initial drum opening, the pattern follows the guitar and bass lines with several variations.

Bars 1–2 | *Buzz rolls*
Buzz rolls can be achieved by manipulating the drumstick and allowing both sticks to bounce naturally on the drum head. This technique requires daily practice and with practise you will be able to perform consistent sounding buzz rolls within a few weeks. Pay attention to the time signature change in the second bar and do not forget to count each quarter note in this section (see Fig. 1).

Bars 5–8 | *Riff*
The drum pattern follows the rhythmic phrasing of the other instruments. Try listening to it, tapping it and even singing it before attempting to play it on the kit. Sync your hands and ensure that any unnecessary flams are avoided. The kick drum is placed on all the sixteenth notes between the ones that are played by the hands. Apart from the speed, the main challenge is keeping this sixteenth-note phrase accurate and fluent. From bar 9 the right hand moves to play on the crash cymbal.

Intro/Main groove (Bars 11–21)

The main groove consists of eighth-note ride cymbals and a varied snare and kick drum patterns. Practise each bar separately to ensure that the specific challenges are tackled before putting it all together.

Verse (Bars 22–29)

The verse has a similar groove to the intro but the right hand moves between the open hi-hat and ride. The structure of the part and number of bars played on each drum voice is slightly unorthodox, so pay close attention to the chart.

Bar 23 | *Hand movement*
In this bar the right hand needs to move smoothly between the open hi-hat, snare and crash. Ensure that your hand movements are accurate, consistent and performed in time.

Chorus (Bars 30–37) & Bridge (Bars 38–43)

While this section is primarily played on the ride, there are also syncopated pushes on the crash and sixteenth-note fills.

Bar 31 | *Fill*
The fill in the second part of this bar can be confusing at first. Start by planning the sticking that you prefer to use. Most drummers would prefer to start with their leading hand. If your leading hand is the right you will simply play R L on the snare, R L on the high tom and follow with kick drum, snare flam and kick drum (see Fig. 2). Experiment and use the sticking option which suits your technique best. Note that the fill starts on the second sixteenth note of the third beat. Counting the beats throughout will help with your understanding of the rhythm of the fill.

Bar 32 | *Syncopated push*
The sixteenth-note push is played on the crash and kick drum. Choosing which hand to play the crash with is very much dependant on your set up. If you have one crash it will be easier to hit the crash with the left hand (assuming the right plays the ride), but if you have more crashes you can choose to play both cymbals with the same hand, saving the effort of constantly moving the hand between cymbals.

Solo (Bars 44–56)

There is a four bar drum solo that prepares for the guitar solo build up which leads to the end of the piece.

Bars 44–47 | *Drum solo*
Aim to make the solo distinct from the groove sections. The rhythmic phrase used in the intro can be your starting point but ensure to develop the solo stylistically from there.

Bars 48–56 | *Guitar solo*
The development in these bars should be more groove-based. Listen to the backing track and see what musical interaction can be created. Pay attention to the cymbal roll and final choked crash in bar 56.

Fig. 1: Buzz rolls

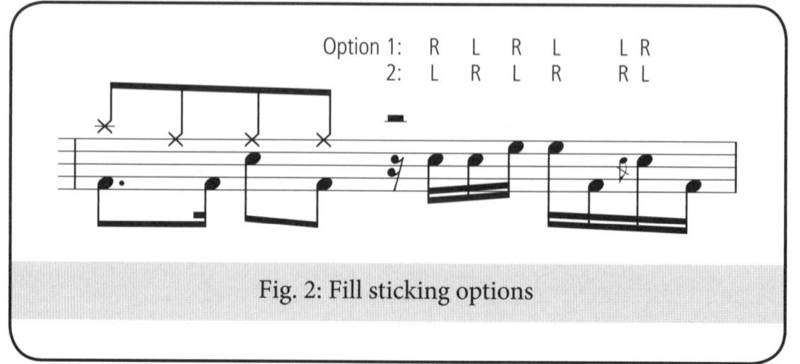

Fig. 2: Fill sticking options

System Of A Down

SONG TITLE: CHOP SUEY!
ALBUM: TOXICITY
RELEASED: 2001
LABEL: AMERICAN
GENRE: METAL

PERSONNEL: SERJ TANKIAN (VOX+KEYS)
DARON MALAKIAN (GTR)
SHAVO ODADJAN (BASS)
JOHN DOLMAYAN (DRUMS)

UK CHART PEAK: 17
US CHART PEAK: 76

BACKGROUND INFO

'Chop Suey!' is the first single off *Toxicity*, the second album by Armenian-American metal band System of a Down. The song features a number of sections: an intro featuring a complex drum groove played around the snare and toms; a full ahead metal verse, punctuated by fast stabs and *tacit* sections, and a more lyrical chorus. The performance requires versatility, power and an awareness of dynamics. The player featured here is John Dolmayan.

THE BIGGER PICTURE

Toxicity was top of the album charts in America at the time of the 9/11 attacks in 2001. 'Chop Suey!' (originally slated to be called 'Suicide') was released in November of the same year and was shunned by many radio stations on account of its lyrical subject matter and this may account for its relatively low chart peak in the US.

On the flip side, the single earned the band its first Grammy nomination and it remains one of their most covered (and parodied) songs. *Toxicity* dominates the band's live sets and has become one of their most popular records, having notched up 12 million worldwide sales and rising.

NOTES

Beirut born Dolmayan joined System of a Down in 1998 after the band's original drummer, Ontironik 'Andy' Kahchaturian broke his hand. He learnt his trade following his saxophonist father around gigs and copying the drum grooves he witnessed as well as learning from classic 60s and 70s rock tracks. He cites Keith Moon as one of his main influences, along with Stuart Copeland and John Bonham. His playing shows versatility, fast and furious one minute, calm and laid back the next, as well as power. He is comfortable with both jazz-influenced grooves and straight ahead metal hammering. In addition to his SOAD work, Dolmayan also plays in a spin-off band, Scars on Broadway.

RECOMMENDED LISTENING

Toxicity is full of instant metal classics, including the title track (another furious, full-on drumming workout), 'Aerials' and 'Prison Song'. Shortly after, mp3 versions of album outtakes escaped into the public domain and were quickly dubbed by fans *Toxicity II*. These were re-recorded and the results released in 2002 as *Steal this Album!* The band were awarded their first Grammy for 'B.Y.O.B.', the standout track from *Mesmerize* (2004).

Chop Suey!

System Of A Down

Words by Serj Tankian & Daron Malakian

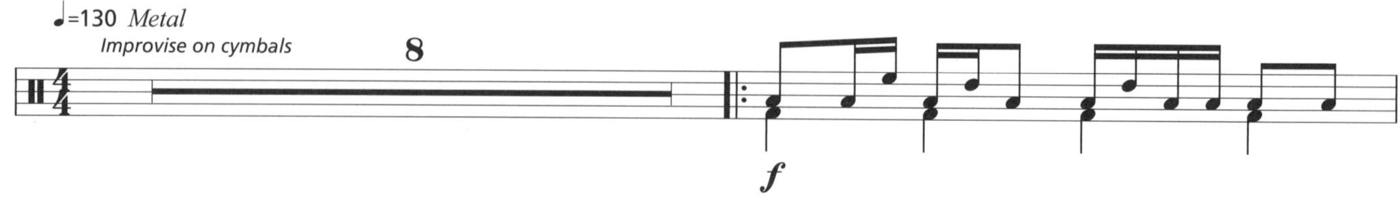

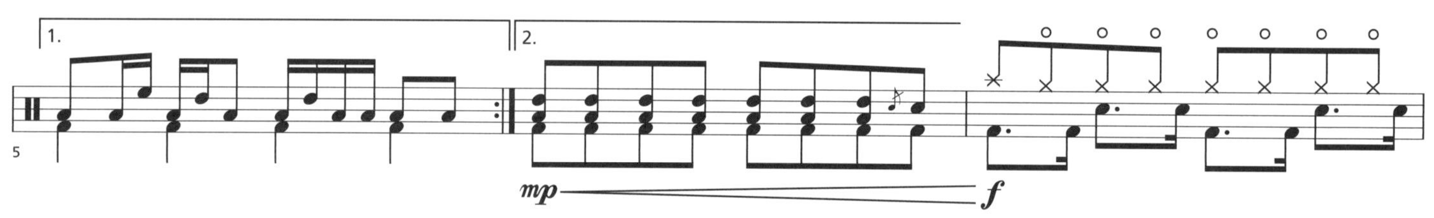

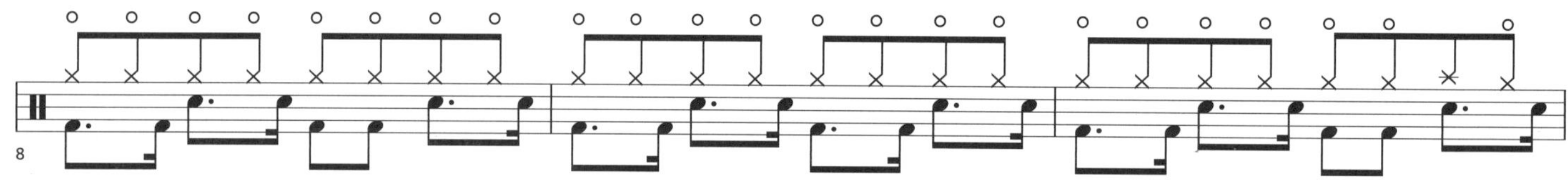

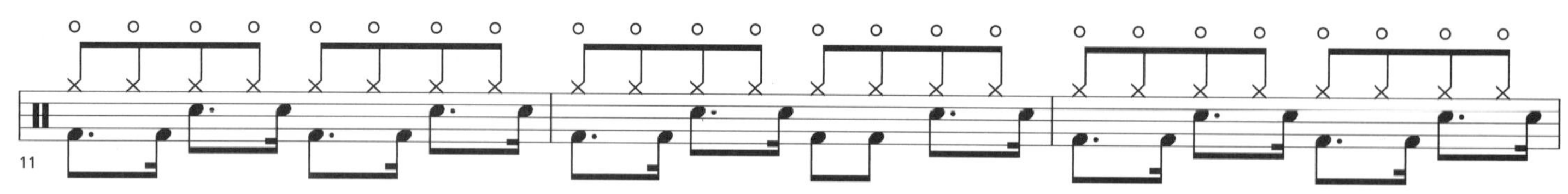

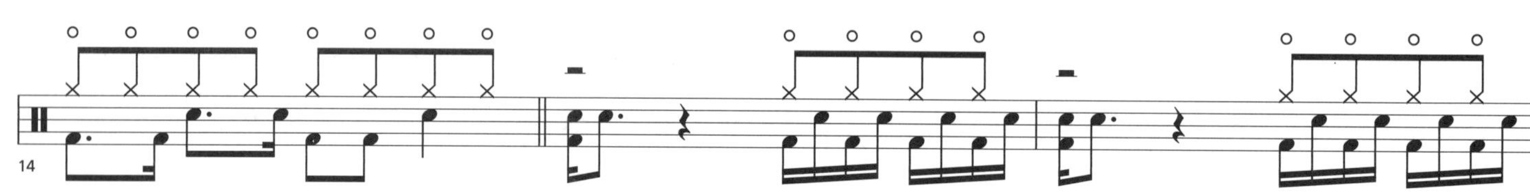

Music by Daron Malakian

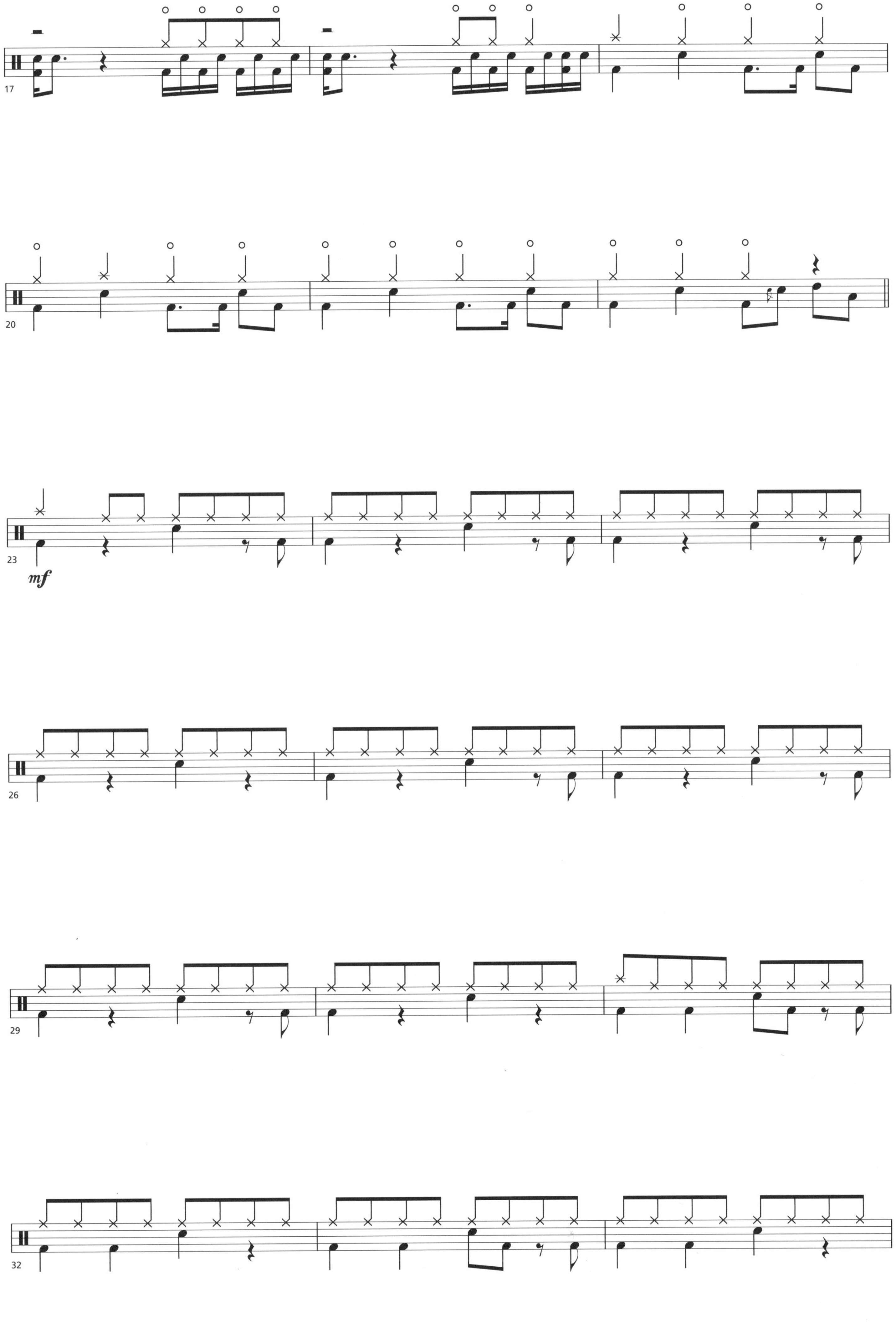

17

20

23

mf

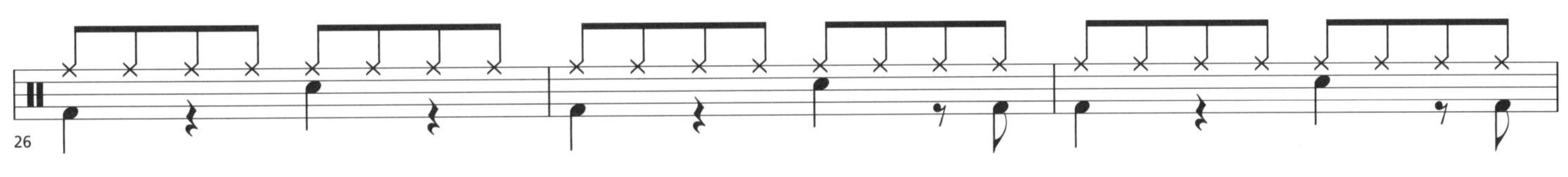

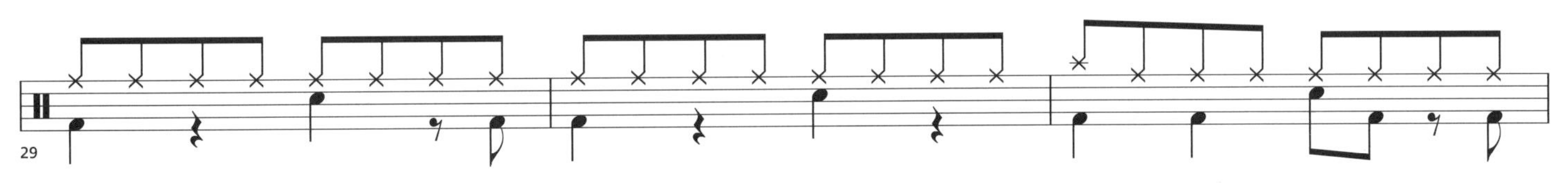

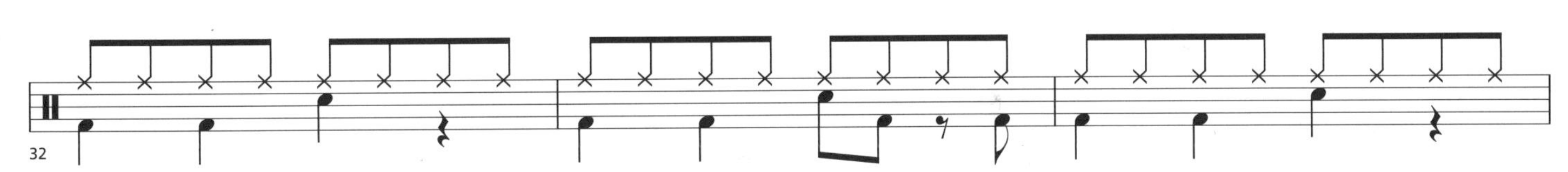

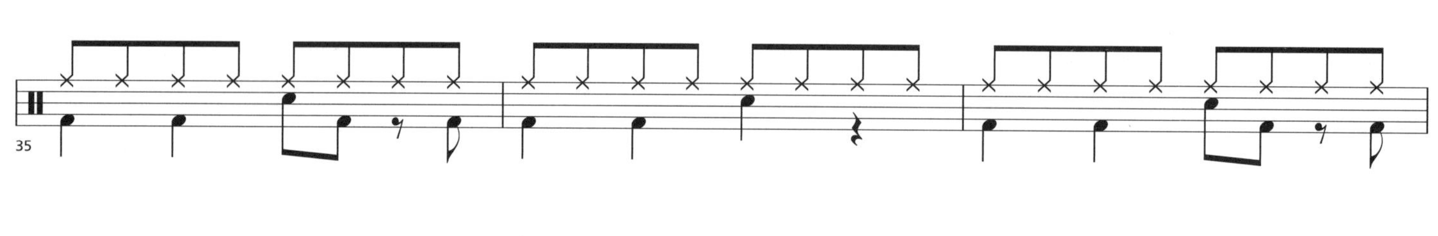
35

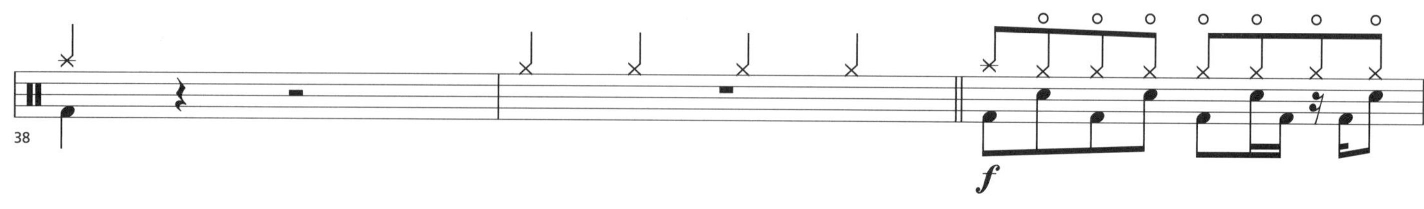
38
f

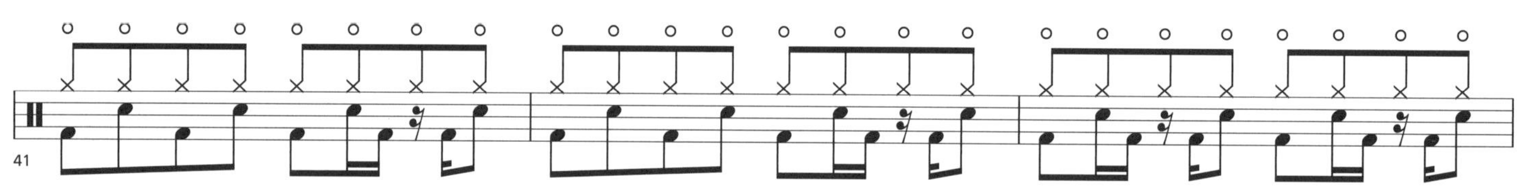
41

Fill
Fill
Fill
Fill
44

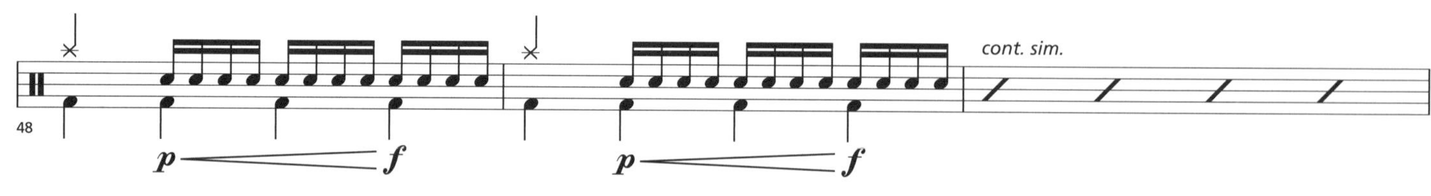
cont. sim.
48
p
f
p
f

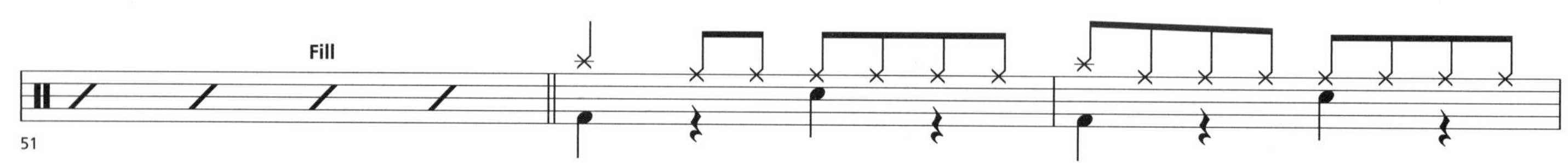
Fill
51

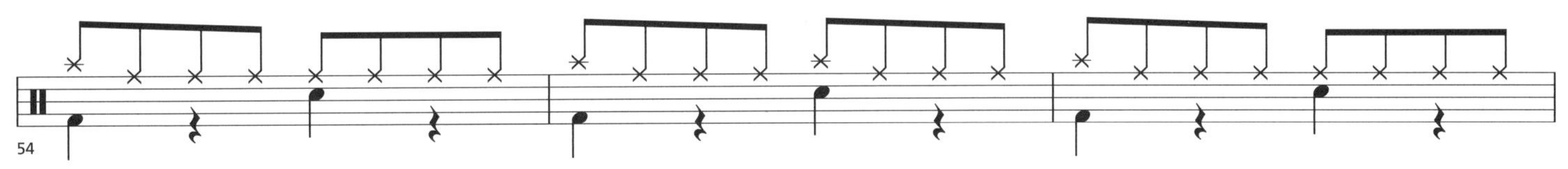
54

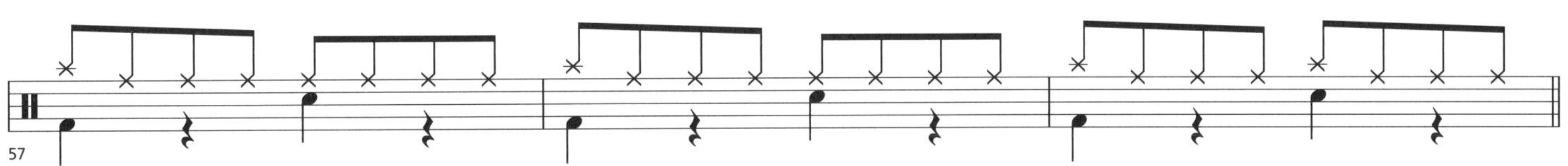
57

Develop
60

64

68

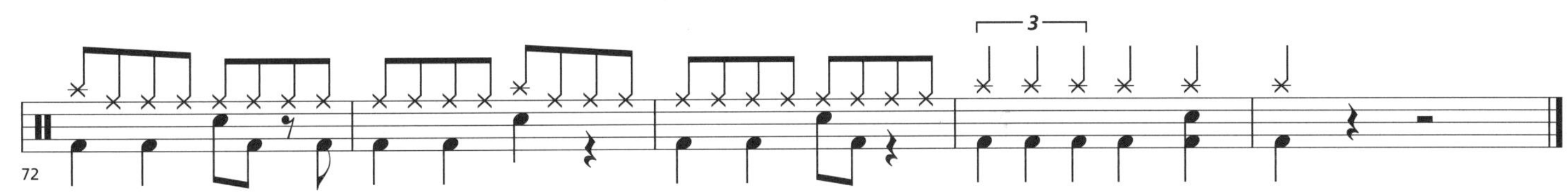
3
72

Walkthrough

Intro (Bars 1–14)

The intro is split into three distinct sections which are outlined below. Work on them individually and then practise putting them all together.

Bar 1 | *Intro cymbals*
Although the original version features very little drumming in the initial eight bars, the examined part allows you to build the mood with improvised cymbal patterns. Various length cymbal rolls and rhythmic patterns with different cymbal combinations will work best.

Bars 2–6 | *Intro toms*
Take some time to get to grips with the rhythmic phrase played with the hands. Next, work out the best sticking option. Once you're comfortable with this, add the quarter-note kick drum and increase the speed. Use the right hand on the floor tom and move the left hand between the high tom and medium tom. However, feel free to adapt the suggested sticking according to your technique. Pay attention to the dynamic build up in bar 6 that leads to the following section (see Fig. 1).

Bars 7–14 | *Intro groove*
This groove consists of heavy open hi-hats and some unorthodox snare and kick drum patterns. Ensure that all sixteenth notes are accurately placed between the eighth-note hi-hat and crashes are played with togetherness.

Verse (Bars 15–22)

The verse consists of a combination of challenging grooves that musically follow the vocal and guitar parts.

Bar 15 | *Blast beat*
The second part of this bar introduces a very popular groove borrowed from extreme metal, the 'blast beat'. In order to execute this well, you need to link the open hi-hat with the kick drum and place the snare in between each hi-hat stroke. This will require advanced coordination, mainly because of the fast tempo. The second challenge is the pattern played on the first beat. Try playing the two sixteenth notes on the snare with alternate sticking and link the kick drum with the first. Ensure that this is synchronised well with the click as well as the guitars (see Fig. 2).

Bar 20 | *Crash on '2'*
In this bar you will have to hit the crash cymbal with the first snare (on the second beat of the bar). The most straightforward way of doing this will be to use the right hand to hit the crash and maintain the left hand on the snare. Ensure that the hands movement is fluent and does not affect the sync with the backing track.

Chorus (Bars 23–39)

The chorus groove is focused on the ride cymbal and a completely different mood needs to be created. Reduce the overall dynamic level fluently and concentrate on capturing the right feel for the groove.

Bridge (Bars 40–51)

Another challenging and fun section of the piece. The grooves are slightly simplified and the part has been edited in order to allow you to solo.

Bars 44–47 | *Improvised fills*
The crash hit at the beginning of each bar should help you stay in sync with the backing track. In between these hits, you need to improvise around the kit showing your musicality and stylistic understanding.

Bars 48–51 | *Crescendo fills*
The sixteenth notes on the snare should be played with alternate sticking. Double sticking is possible but will not achieve the same intensity as alternate. You will be able to create natural crescendo if you start the fill at the edge of the drum head and gradually move towards the middle.

Chorus (Bars 52–77)

The groove is similar to the first chorus but allows you to develop the part. Remember that this is not a drum solo and the feel of the section must be maintained.

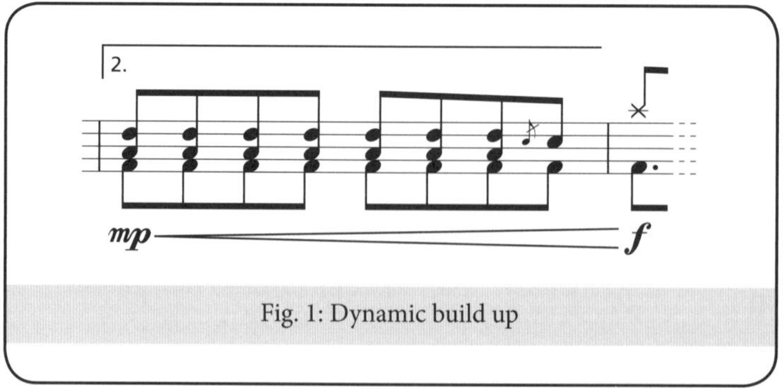

Fig. 1: Dynamic build up

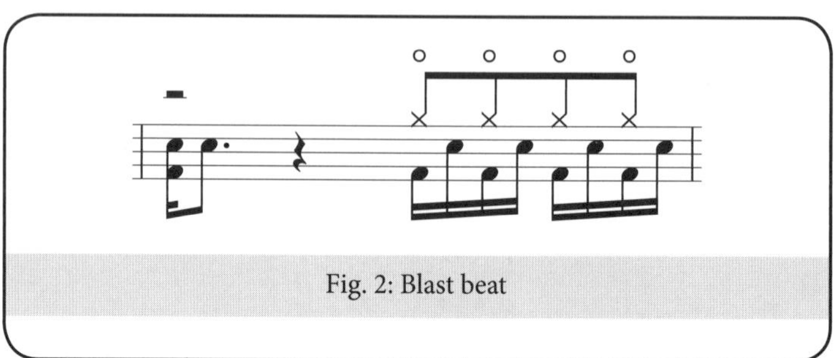
Fig. 2: Blast beat

The Jimi Hendrix Experience

SONG TITLE: HEY JOE
ALBUM: N/A
RELEASED: 1966
LABEL: TRACK/POLYDOR
GENRE: ROCK

PERSONNEL: JIMI HENDRIX (GTR+VOX)
NOEL REDDING (BASS)
MITCH MITCHELL (DRUMS)

UK CHART PEAK: 6
US CHART PEAK: N/A

BACKGROUND INFO

The Jimi Hendrix Experience's version of 'Hey Joe' was their first single and helped launch them in the UK. The Hendrix sound was born complete from the start in this power trio that featured the energetic drumming of the late Mitch Mitchell.

THE BIGGER PICTURE

Hendrix's signature riffing and chord play rest on the firm foundations of Mitchell's confident, tight and fast groove work. This perfectly complements the guitar hero's passion and trickery as well as driving what is a fairly repetitive song along at breakneck pace. This interplay between them set the pattern for much of what followed in the band's first album and tracks such as 'Red House' and 'Fire' stand out as much for the stickmanship as the guitar playing. Mitchell, like many British drummers of the time, was heavily jazz-influenced.

Hendrix had huge respect for Mitch's abilities and liked to record guide tracks in the studio with Mitch and no-one else which explains the tightness of the interplay on the recordings.

NOTES

It could all have been so different. Mitch got the Hendrix gig on the toss of a coin (Aynsley Dunbar was the loser on this occasion). Mitch had previously been a ubiquitous sessioneer and also featured in the Rolling Stones' doomed 1968 *Rock 'n' Roll Circus* film where he played in the 'Dirty Mac' supergroup that also featured John Lennon on guitar and vocals and Keith Richards on bass. After the death of Hendrix, Mitch kept the flame alive with tribute gigs and producing some of the immediate posthumous releases. He was the last member of the Experience to die, in November 2008 aged 61.

RECOMMENDED LISTENING

1967's *Are You Experienced* contains more classic tracks than most artists' entire greatest hits collections, among them: 'Foxy Lady', 'Manic Depression', 'Red House' and 'Fire'. The 1968 follow up, *Axis: Bold As Love* is equally stacked, boasting 'Little Wing', 'If 6 was 9' and 'Spanish Castle Magic'. *Electric Ladyland* was the last release with the original lineup and contains 'Voodoo Child (Slight Return)', 'Crosstown Traffic' and their sublime cover of Bob Dylan's 'All Along The Watchtower'.

Hey Joe

The Jimi Hendrix Experience

Words & Music by Billy Roberts

Swung 16ths

21

Swung 16ths

24

Swung 16ths

27

Fill

30

33

Fill

Develop

35

38

41

mp

44

f

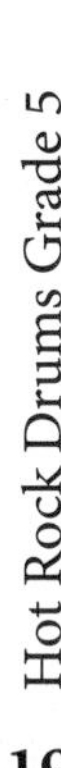

Walkthrough

Intro (Bars 1–2)

The intro mostly consists of solo guitar, but a sixteenth-note drum fill introduces the rest of the song.

Bars 1–2 | *Sixteenth-note fill*
Count the beats in these bars to ensure that all quarter-note hi-hats are accurately placed. The fill consists of sixteenth-note strokes around the kit. Alternate sticking will work best here, but feel free to adapt according to your own technique and set up.

Verse (Bars 3–34)

The constant change between straight eighth notes and swung sixteenth notes is the main challenge in this section. The fills in this examined version have been simplified but the original feel was maintained.

Bars 3–4 | *Opening and closing the hi-hat*
In this groove the hi-hat should be opened on every eighth note that is played before the backbeat. The hi-hat is closed on the backbeat so pay attention to the togetherness between the hi-hat and snare.

Bars 5–6 | *Swung sixteenth notes*
The jazz element is introduced in the form of swung sixteenth notes. It will be helpful to practise this section separately at a slower tempo. Initially, play all sixteenth notes straight and then try swinging the sixteenth notes. It will be extremely helpful for you to become familiar with both straight and swing feels before attempting this piece.

Bar 10 | *Sixteenth-note triplet fill*
In this fill you will need to divide the quarter note into a sixteenth-note triplet (equal to one eighth note) and an eighth note. Listen to the full version of this song in order to understand the rhythm aurally. Use alternate sticking and start with your right hand to ensure that all the strokes are even (see Fig. 1).

Bar 18 | *Sextuplet*
On the last beat of this bar there is a sextuplet (or two sixteenth-note triplets). This means that you have to play six even strokes over one quarter note. You will need to use a highly secure wrist motion or basic fingers technique. Research both methods thoroughly and choose the one that works best for you.

Bar 26 | *Hand & foot combinations*
Fills that involve hand and foot combinations are challenging, but also musical. Practise this fill at various speeds as well as moving it around the kit. This will help build your technique. In this fill you will need to move clockwise from the snare to the toms, while maintaining the sextuplet rhythm. This is an excellent opportunity to demonstrate consistent balance between hands and feet.

Bar 32 | *Flams between drums*
On the third beat of the bar you will be required to perform flams between drums. The concept is exactly the same as performing a flam on one drum. However, as flams on two different drums are less common, close attention needs to be paid to the timing and accuracy. Remember that the main stroke of the flam should be played on the beat and the grace note slightly before (see Fig. 2).

Guitar solo (Bars 35–45)

The guitar solo section leading to the end of this piece allows you to develop and perform some of your own fills.

Bar 35 | *Basic groove*
This groove is ride-led and consists of simple kick drum and snare patterns. You should play this bar exactly as written but then develop it, in a stylistically appropriate way, from the following bar. Remember that this is a guitar solo so you still need to hold the groove and provide the rhythmic foundation for the band.

Bars 43–45 | *Grand finale*
Dropping the dynamic level in bar 43 is very important as it allows you to build dynamically from there. The combination of groove and fills needs to be practised separately, remembering to keep the eighth-note kick drums underneath the sixteenth-note fill in bar 43.

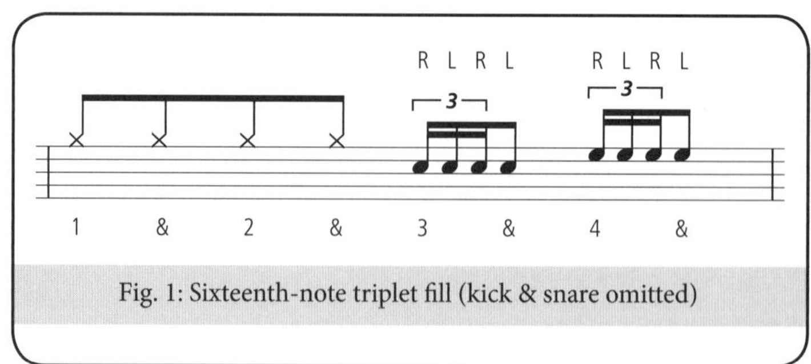

Fig. 1: Sixteenth-note triplet fill (kick & snare omitted)

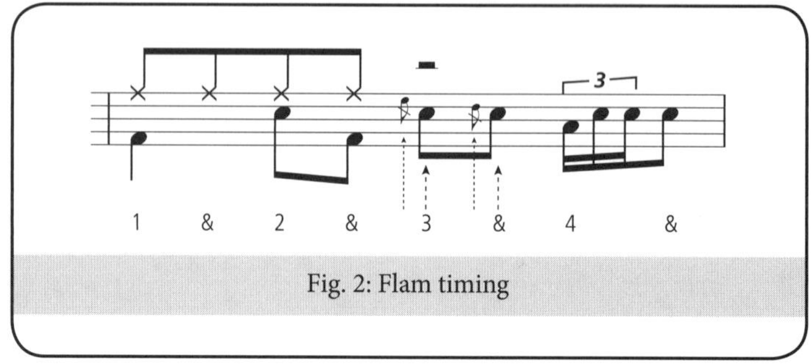

Fig. 2: Flam timing

SONG TITLE: LATE IN THE EVENING
ALBUM: ONE TRICK PONY
RELEASED: 1980
LABEL: WARNER BROS.
GENRE: LATIN BLUES

PERSONNEL: PAUL SIMON (VOX)
STEVE GADD (DRUMS)
ERIC GALE (GTR)
TONY LEVIN (BASS)
RICHARD TEE (PNO)

UK CHART PEAK: 17
US CHART PEAK: 12

BACKGROUND INFO

'Late in the Evening' is the most successful single off Paul Simon's 1980 album *One Trick Pony* that accompanied a film of the same name. The drummer on this track was ace American percussionist Steve Gadd who appeared alongside some of the cream of New York session players. All of the band members appear in the film in the role of backing musicians to the central character played by Paul Simon. Interpolated into the groove is a 'Mozambique', a form of Cuban dance rhythm that gives the song its evocative Latin sensibility. Interestingly, Gadd plays the part holding two drum sticks in each hand, which, as he explains in drum masterclasses, is done in order to make it sound as though the piece is being played by "more than one guy".

THE BIGGER PICTURE

Although released at the same time, the film and the album of *One Trick Pony* should be seen as musically separate: the album is definitely *not* the film soundtrack. Gadd and his colleagues had already played together in a band called Stuff when they performed on the record, and they had released a number of albums with this line up in the late 70s and early 80s.

NOTES

Steve Gadd is one of the most successful and well respected drummers of his generation. Principally a jazz specialist, he has played with a range of pop and blues artists including Steely Dan, the Bee Gees, Paul Simon, Chick Corea, Al di Meola, BB King, Eric Clapton, Paul McCartney, George Benson, Frank Sinatra and Bonnie Raitt.

RECOMMENDED LISTENING

Gadd made his name playing with New York songwriting duo Donald Fagan and Walter Becker (Steely Dan) on their jazz influenced *Aja* album in 1977, contributing a distinctive drum break to the coda of the title track (parodied mercilessly by Frank Zappa and Terry Bozio in 'A Little Green Rosetta' on *Joe's Garage*). At the same time, he played straight ahead jazz drums for Chick Corea on the *Friends* (1978) and *Three Quartets* (1981).

He can also be found on Paul McCartney's *Tug of War* (1982) and *Pipes of Peace* (1983). More recently, he has played with Art Garfunkel on *Some Enchanted Evening* (2007) and James Taylor on *October Road* (2001) as well as two very popular albums of classic cover versions.

Late In The Evening

Paul Simon

Words & Music by Paul Simon

♩=120 *Mozambique*

p

3

6

mp

9

mf

12

15

f

18

21

24

Fill

27

cont. sim.

mf

Solo (8 bars)
Fill
Fill

Walkthrough

Open sections

There are many open sections in this piece and it is important that you follow the specific instructions in each one of them. *Cont. sim.* sections allow you to vary the written patterns, and open fills and solo sections will require improvisation. The essence of the song needs to be maintained: therefore listening to music that uses the mozambique rhythm, along with live performances of this track with Steve Gadd on drums will give you creative ideas.

Verse (Bars 1–14)

The verse introduces the main groove of the piece, the mozambique. Pay attention to the dynamic changes and fill in bar 14. This 14 bar section follows an unorthodox structure of five, five and four bars. It is important to listen to the original song and get familiar with the musical patterns played by the other instruments.

Bar 1 | *Mozambique*
This pattern is based on a challenging hands pattern with consistent quarter-note kick drum underneath. After the initial hit on the first beat using both hands, follow this sticking: 1 (both hands) R L R R L R L R R L R R L R. Place your right hand in position to hit the side rim of the floor tom. Remember that the left hand will be moving between the high, medium and floor toms.

The toms should be played in the middle for maximum projection and the side rim should be hit with the shoulder of the stick. If you prefer, try playing the side of the shell of the floor tom instead as it will produce a similar sound. Choose the one that feels more comfortable and practise producing a consistent sound. The quarter-note kick drums can be your anchor and it will be helpful to count the beats in each bar while practising this groove (see Fig. 1).

Bar 6 | *Moderately quiet*
This is the first dynamic change of the section. From moderately quiet you change to moderately loud (bar 11) and crescendo to loud in bar 14. Remember that velocity changes can naturally be created by lifting the sticks higher or lower before striking the drum heads. These subtle changes might require some practise to master.

Chorus (Bars 15–26)

The mozambique groove is moved to the bell of the ride cymbal and some stylistic fills as well as improvised are introduced.

Bar 15 | *Riding the bell*
The bell becomes the leading sound in this section. Therefore, the sound must be dominant and consistent. Play the bell with the shoulder part of the stick and keep the stick close to the cymbal to achieve consistent sound. The left hand pattern and sticking is exactly the same as before, so focus on the balance between kit parts.

Bar 18 | *Sixteenth-note rest*
This fill will give you an idea of suitable variations in this style. Resting on the first sixteenth note in each beat can be straightforward, as long as you count throughout and understand the rhythmic phrase. As before, the kick drum will be your anchor and you should use the sticking that feels most natural to you.

Bar 22 | *Dotted rhythms*
A dot next to the note means that you have to add half of the value of the original note *i.e.* in this example the dotted eighth note is worth three quarters of a beat (or eighth note plus a sixteenth note). The rhythm in this stylistic fill is syncopated and challenging. You need to play on the first and last sixteenth notes of beat 1 and the offbeat of beat 2. The same rhythm can be found in the third and fourth beats. In this case, listening to the full recording and singing the rhythm might be the most straightforward approach (see Fig. 2).

Bars 41–48 | *Drum solo*
Maintaining the quarter-note kick drum and soloing with the hands will be the most straightforward and stylistic approach. The rhythmic horns enter in the middle of bar 44. Make yourself familiar with the horns phrasing and try to incorporate some of these in your solo. From bar 45 you can either continue with the full drum solo approach or return to the groove and add improvised fills where appropriate.

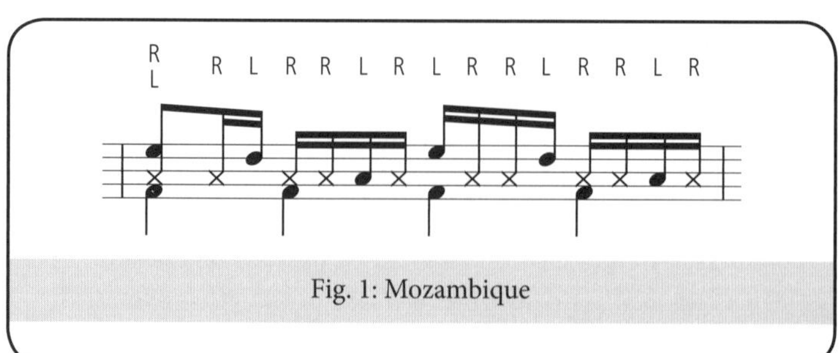

Fig. 1: Mozambique

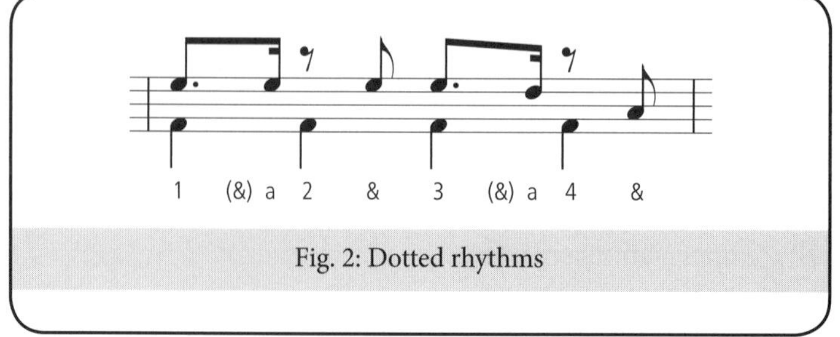

Fig. 2: Dotted rhythms

SONG TITLE: MASTER OF PUPPETS
ALBUM: MASTER OF PUPPETS
RELEASED: 1986
LABEL: ELEKTRA
GENRE: METAL

PERSONNEL: JAMES HETFIELD (GTR+VOX)
KIRK HAMMETT (GTR)
CLIFF BURTON (BASS)
LARS ULRICH (DRUMS)

UK CHART PEAK: N/A
US CHART PEAK: N/A

BACKGROUND INFO

'Master Of Puppets' is the lead single from the third Metallica album of the same name. This classic early-period Metallica song features their signature fast, tight riffing underpinned by a syncopated drum groove full of rhythmic variation and lightning quick accented snare stabs courtesy of Lars Ulrich. At more than eight minutes in length, the full version of the song is an intense workout requiring power, control and stamina.

THE BIGGER PICTURE

Master Of Puppets was Metallica's first album for a major label and was followed by their first tours outside of the US. The effect of major label input was instantly noticeable: a more polished sound and greater songwriting inventiveness than seen on the records immediate predecessor *Ride The Lightening* (1984). Despite having no radio play and no video releases, the album notched up over 500,000 in sales in the US alone and was a hit with both fans and critics. Metallica entered the big league with a record that many consider the best metal album of all time. In recent years at several live shows the band have treated their audience to a performance of *Master Of Puppets* in its entirety.

NOTES

Tennis' loss is music's gain. Lars Ulrich, an upcoming tennis pro from Denmark, placed an ad for a band in a local Californian newspaper in 1981 that was answered initially by James Hetfield. The heart and soul of the band is essentially the creative rivalry between these two giant personalities, both masters of their game. The tracks on *Master Of Puppets* reveal just how talented a player Ulrich is: speed, accuracy and power are all within his compass and he has complete control of rhythmic variations, changes in time signature, syncopation and groove displacement. He hardly ever plays the same groove without some form of development and it is this rhythmic interplay behind the riffing and powerplay out front that makes Metallica's output of this period so compelling.

RECOMMENDED LISTENING

Master Of Puppets is replete with thrash metal classics, including 'Battery', 'Welcome Home (Sanitarium)', 'Disposable Heroes' and 'Damage, Inc.' *Master* was followed by *...And Justice For All* (1988) and then by the monster that is the *Metallica* (or 'Black') album of 1991 that features 'Enter Sandman' and 'Nothing Else Matters', after which the band was one of the biggest on the planet.

Master Of Puppets

Metallica

Words & Music by James Hetfield, Lars Ulrich, Cliff Burton & Kirk Hammett

♩=220 *Metal*

Choke

4

Choke

8

Choke

12

Choke

mp — *f*

Solo on repeat

Choke

16

20

24

28

Choke
cont. sim.

63

66

69

72

76

Fill

80

Fill

84

Fill

88

Choke

Choke

Choke
Choke
Choke
Choke

Walkthrough

Intro (Bars 1–19)

This section includes many rests and stylistic fills. There is also an opportunity for you to improvise before the groove enters in bar 20.

Bar 1 | *Choke cymbal*
This is a common technique in metal as well as other styles such as funk and latin. It refers to creating a short attack sound from the cymbal. In order to perform this correctly, hit the cymbal with one hand and catch it with your other hand soon after to stop it from ringing. The choke technique can be performed on any cymbal but is most effective on crashes.

Bar 2 | *Counting rests*
In this bar you have to play three consecutive quarter-note crash hits (with kick drum) and rest on the fourth beat. It is crucial that you keep counting and maintain a secure pulse. Counting is also necessary in bars where you have nothing to play such as bar 3.

Bars 13–15 | *Crescendo fill*
The fill consists of eighteen consecutive eighth notes on the snare, building gradually from ***mp*** (moderately quiet) to ***f*** (loud). Starting the fill at the top of the snare drum and moving gradually towards the middle will assist you in creating this dynamic change naturally.

Bar 16 | *Hi hat foot*
From the second beat in bar 16 you will notice a cymbal note notation at the bottom of the stave. This refers to playing the hi-hat pedal with the foot. It is common in metal to play this with the heel up technique as it produces a louder and more decisive sound. It can be played with heel down.

Bar 19 | *Dotted rhythms*
In bar 19 some of the crashes are dotted notes. This means that the value of the note is longer by 50 per cent. This rhythmic phrase requires you to hit on the first beat and the offbeat of the second and fourth beats. It is a good idea to become familiar with this phrase as it will repeat many times in the piece (see Fig. 1).

Bar 16 (on repeat) | *Soloing*
On the repeat of this section you need to improvise. Aim for a stylistic combination of fills and an individual development of a certain rhythmic phrase. Listen to the full version and similar Metallica tracks for inspiration.

Verse (Bars 39–72)

This is the most challenging as well as the most identifiable section of the song.

Bar 42 | *5/8 time signature*
The 5/8 time signature indicates that there are five eighth notes in this bar. The main challenge is counting this bar at a fast tempo and moving between the time signatures with fluency. You will be playing on the first, second and fourth eighth notes in the bar before returning to the 4/4 groove. It might be easier to listen to the full backing track a few times before attempting to play it (see Fig. 2).

Bar 55 | *Cont. sim.*
Remember that this is not a solo section, but requires you to make minor variations of the groove.

Pre-chorus (Bars 72–89)
The section that leads to the chorus is all in 4/4 time but includes many crash hits, notated fills and improvised fills.

Bar 72 | *Crash movement*
The hectic crash work in this section can be played in several ways. Depending on your technique, set up and level of fluency around the kit, decide on the way which works best for you.

Bar 79 | *Improvised fill*
As always, it is important that your improvised fills are individual and stylistic.

Chorus (Bars 89–112)

The time signature changes from 4/4 to 2/4 (and vice versa) should not be as challenging as the ones in the verse. However, pay close attention to the click and sync with the backing track at this point.

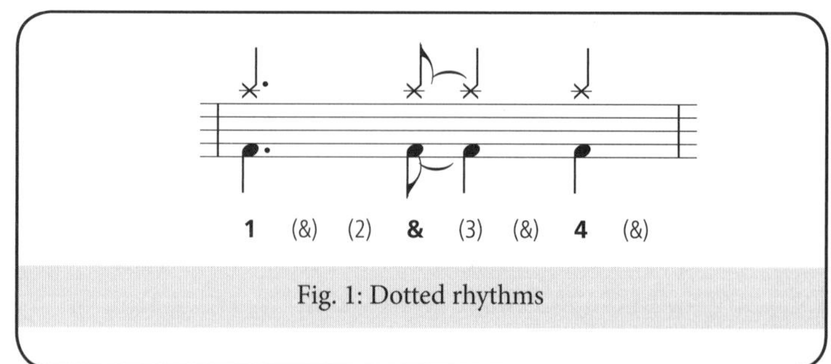

Fig. 1: Dotted rhythms

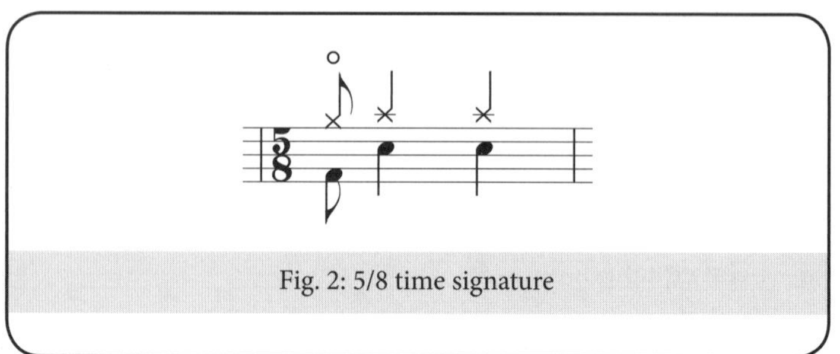
Fig. 2: 5/8 time signature

SONG TITLE: MY GENERATION
ALBUM: MY GENERATION
RELEASED: 1965
LABEL: BRUNSWICK
GENRE: 60S R&B

PERSONNEL: ROGER DALTRY (VOX)
PETE TOWNSHEND (GTR+VOX)
JOHN ENTWISTLE (BASS)
KEITH MOON (DRUMS)

UK CHART PEAK: 2
US CHART PEAK: 74

BACKGROUND INFO

'My Generation' is one of the standout tracks from The Who's debut album of the same name. Few songs written in the 60s encapsulate the youthful rage of the period quite like this one as Townshend spits out his disgust and loathing of the older generation ('hope I die before I get old'). The energy of this band was fuelled by the antics of their irrepressible drummer. Keith Moon is a perennial favourite in polls and lists of the greatest rock drummers of all time, and was inducted into The Rock And Roll Hall Of Fame in 1990 as a member of The Who.

THE BIGGER PICTURE

The Who emerged out of the Mod scene in the early to mid 1960s having grown up together around Ealing in west London. Their brand of 'Maximum R&B', along with their trademark smashing up of their instruments at the end of 'My Generation', marked them out early on as a group of particularly angry young men in a way that differentiated them from their peers. The pairing of the ebullient, fearless Moon with the quieter, classically trained, virtuoso bass player John Entwistle created one of the great rhythm sections in British pop - one that has rarely been equalled.

NOTES

When they made Keith Moon they broke the mould. He was a one-off, both as a person and as a player. The archetypal rock hell-raiser (by the end of the 60s he was banned from just about every hotel chain in America), Moon set the standard for hard-living and fast playing. He played fast and furious on a kit with no hi-hat or ride cymbal, opting instead for many crash cymbals. The keys to Moon's playing were his speed, accuracy and timing: and what, to some ears at least, sounded random and undisciplined, was in fact highly focused.

RECOMMENDED LISTENING

The power of the early Who singles was their trademark and Keith Moon's signature sound can be heard to great effect on 'Substitute' (1966), 'I Can See for Miles' and 'Pictures of Lilly' (both 1967). Later material, such as 'Won't Get Fooled Again', 'Baba O'Riley' (both 1971) and 'Who Are You?' (1978), show Moon in complete command. Keith Moon played the role of drummer J D Clover in the film *That'll be the Day* (1973) that features a close-up burst of the master in action.

My Generation

The Who

Words & Music by Pete Townshend

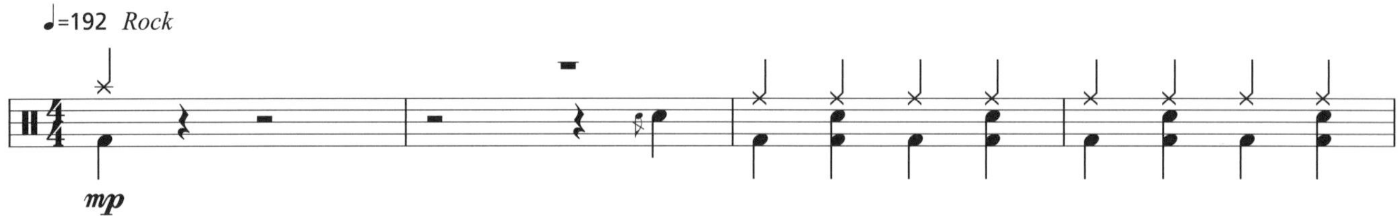

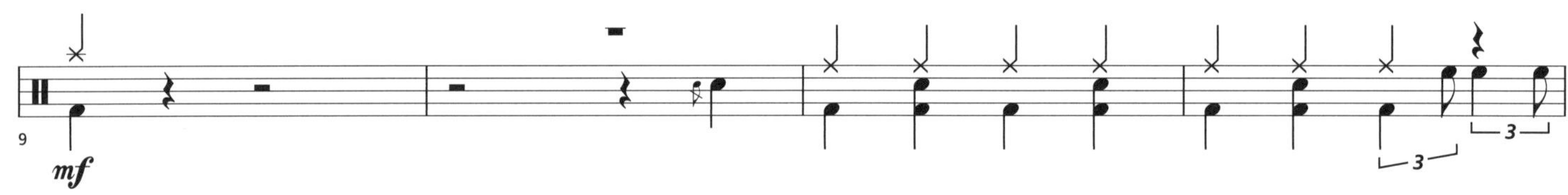

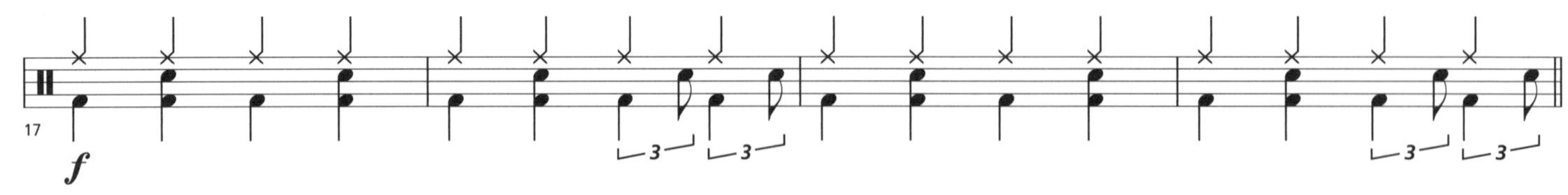

cont. sim.

25

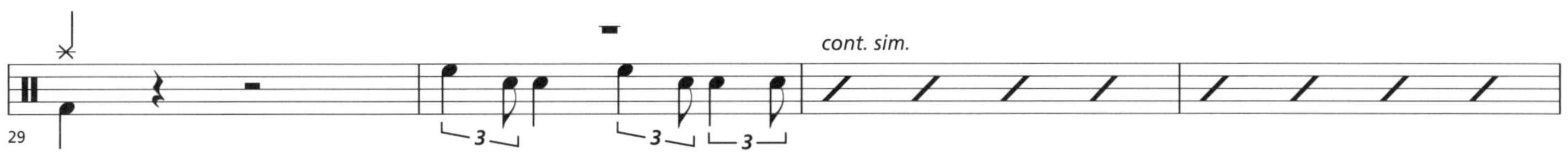

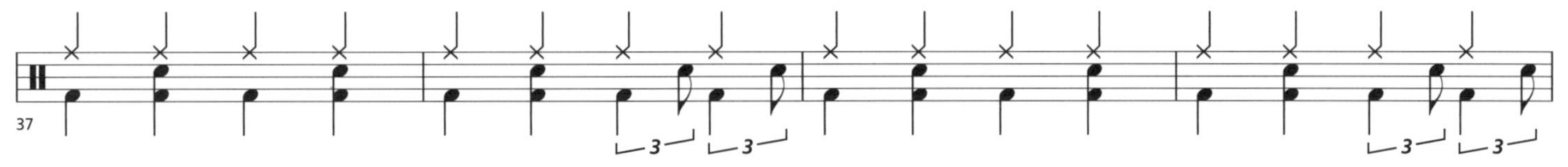

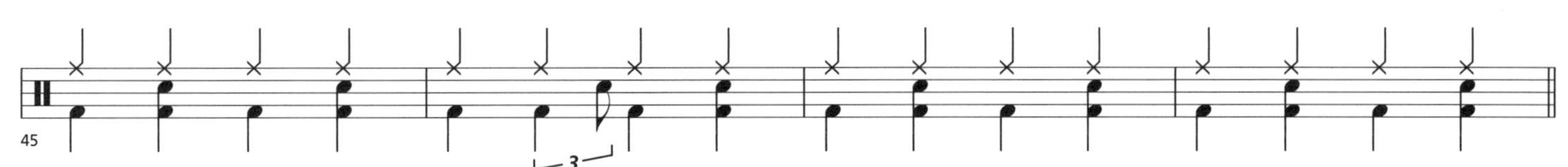

49
53
57
61
65
69
p
f
Solo (18 bars, on repeat only)
73

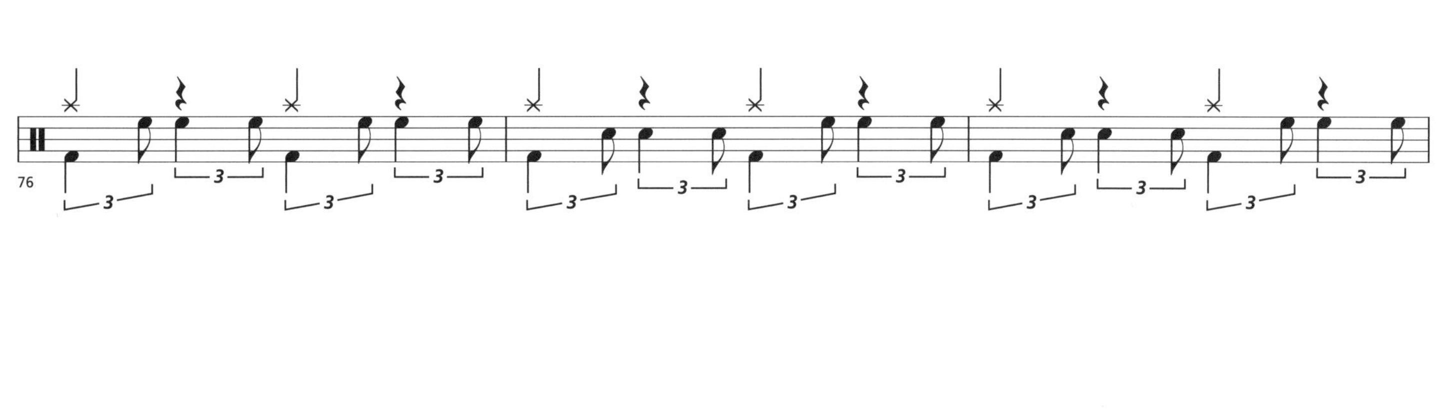
76

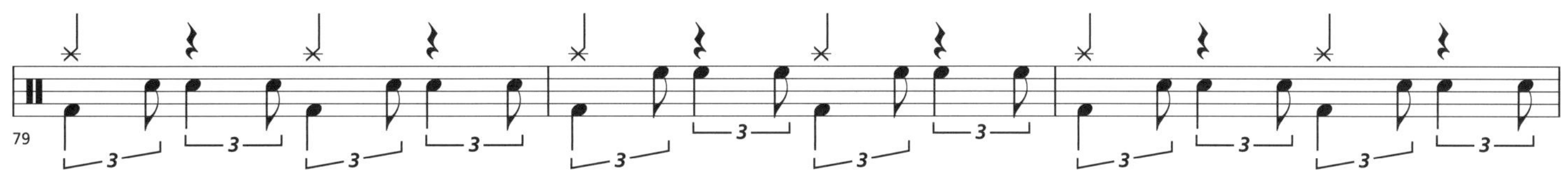
79

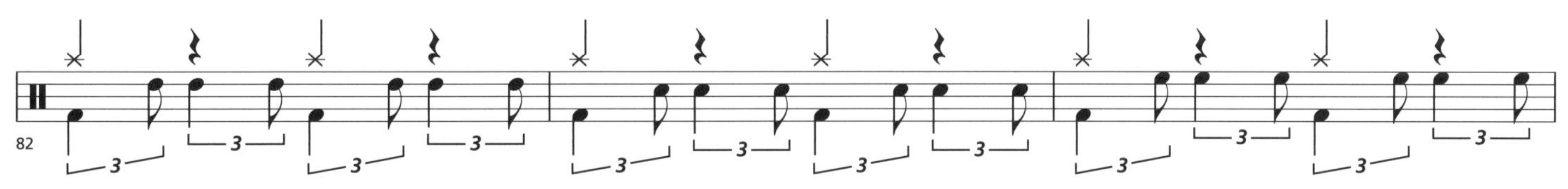
82

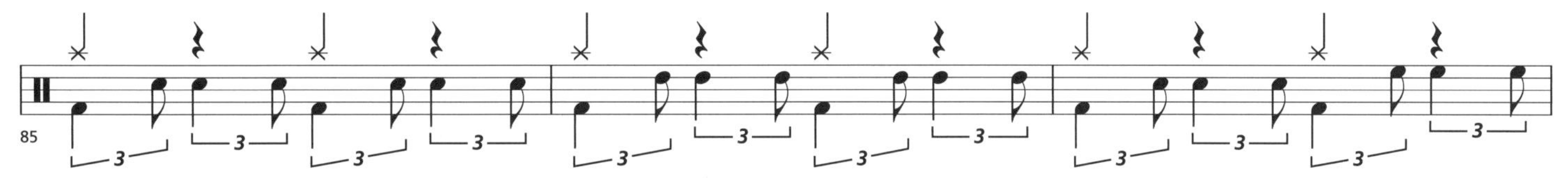
85

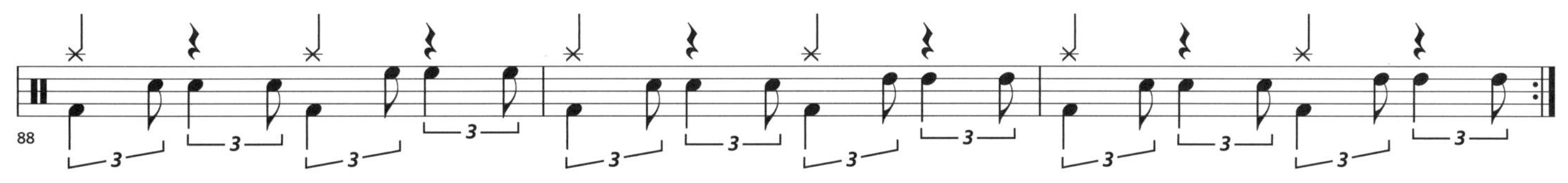
88

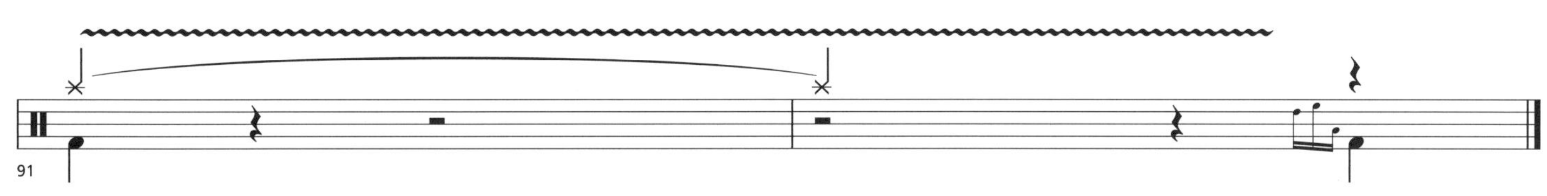
91

Walkthrough

Bass solo (Bars 1–20)

This examined part starts from the bass solo which is situated in the middle of the full part. The groove and breaks follow a four bar structure with some challenging fills. Pay attention to the dynamic changes in this section.

Bars 1–2 | *Crash & Flam*
Hit the initial crash exactly on the first beat and keep counting the beats in both bars. The next stroke is the snare flam on the fourth beat of bar 2, aim to play this with absolute conviction.

Bar 3 | *Ride sound*
If you listen carefully to the original recording or the full backing track you will hear that the ride is played heavily. This is not notated but will demonstrate a high degree of understanding of this style. You will be able to achieve this sound by hitting the ride with the shoulder part of the stick and lifting your hand higher.

Bar 16 | *Triplet fills*
These fills are simplified versions of the originals but still maintain the stylistic integrity. The rhythmic meter is triplets (three equal notes over one quarter note), and the second triplet in each group is missing.

You can also think about it as swung eighth notes, which are most commonly used in jazz music. The suggested sticking here is alternate sticking starting with the right hand and you should focus on accurate timing and balanced projection (see Fig. 1).

Verse & Chorus (Bars 21–48)

This section should be played at the new dynamic level of ***f*** (*forte*, which means loud). The structure, grooves and fills are similar to the previous section. However, some individual variations will be needed.

Bars 23–24 | *Cont. sim.*
The instruction *cont. sim.* (continue similarly) gives you the opportunity to vary these bars. The basic groove and feel should be maintained but minor changes should be played. Here are a few suggestions for variations: i) using a slightly loose hi-hat instead of the ride, ii) adding a few kick drums, iii) replacing the second snare in each bar with two eighth notes on the high tom.

Bar 26 | *Counting triplets*
This is a very challenging entry, as the snare fill starts on the third triplet of the third beat. You will need to count the beats but it will be too fast to count all the triplets. It may help to remember that the entry triplet (third of beat 3) should be placed after an eighth note and before the last sixteenth note in the bar. It also should have the important triplet feel. Practise this repeatedly at a slow tempo until you can play it accurately.

Second Verse & Chorus (Bars 49–72)

This is very similar to the previous section, however there are variations of the fills and an added hi-hat foot part during the breaks.

Bar 49 | *Hi hat foot*
The cymbal note that is placed below the kick drum on the stave refers to playing the hi-hat pedal with the foot. The pattern in this case plays the same as the claps recorded on the backing track. Therefore, listen to the backing track in order to understand which beats needs to be played or carefully follow the notation in the chart. In any case counting the beats during the breaks will ensure that you perform these accurately. Using the heel up technique will help you achieve the right sound from the hi-hat (see Fig. 2).

Outro (Bars 73–92)

When you play this section for the first time you need to follow the notation accurately. However, on the repeat you should improvise around the kit.

It is important to solo with confidence and in keeping with the style. As always, listening to the full version, the original track and drumming by the legendary Keith Moon will point you in the right direction.

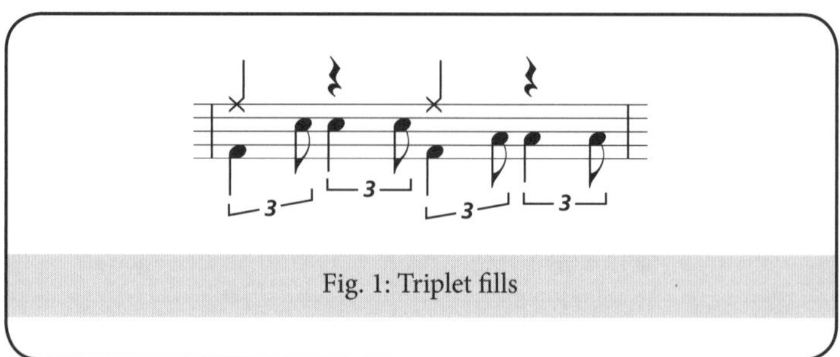

Fig. 1: Triplet fills

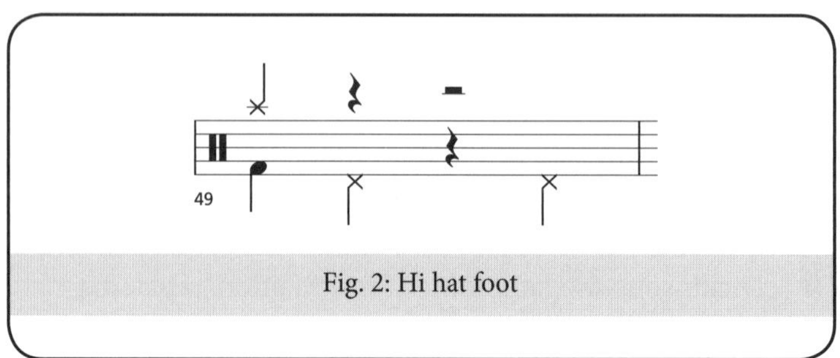

Fig. 2: Hi hat foot

SONG TITLE: THE NUMBER OF THE BEAST
ALBUM: THE NUMBER OF THE BEAST
RELEASED: 1982
LABEL: EMI
GENRE: HEAVY METAL

PERSONNEL: BRUCE DICKINSON (VOX)
DAVE MURRAY (GTR)
ADRIAN SMITH (GTR)
STEVE HARRIS (BASS)
CLIVE BURR (DRUMS)

UK CHART PEAK: 18
US CHART PEAK: N/A

BACKGROUND INFO

'The Number of the Beast' was the second single off Iron Maiden's 1982 album of the same name. This song features a classic operatic vocal from frontman Bruce Dickinson as well as a Vincent Price-esque opening narration provided on the original recording by radio actor Barry Clayton. The drummer featured here in this full ahead early 80s metal track is the unheralded Clive Burr.

THE BIGGER PICTURE

Iron Maiden is one of the behemoths of the New Wave of British Heavy Metal (often abbreviated to NWOBHM) that found huge success in America and elsewhere in the 1980s and is still one of the most popular performing bands in the world today. They are also one of the most prolific with nearly 40 albums to their credit, including eleven live records.

NOTES

Clive Burr was originally a member of the 70s rock band Samson on whose debut album he appears. The band also featured on vocals old Etonian Bruce Dickinson who later joined Iron Maiden, replacing original singer Paul Di'anno, for the recording of *Beast* in 1981. *The Number of the Beast* was Clive Burr's last recording with Iron Maiden before he was replaced by current drummer Nicko McBrain.

RECOMMENDED LISTENING

Burr played on the first three Iron Maiden albums, *Iron Maiden* (1980) and *Killers* (1981) in addition to *The Number of the Beast*. The songs on their debut album were effectively produced by the band after their producer lost interest and left them to it. Many fans still regard 'Phantom of the Opera', 'Iron Maiden' and 'Charlotte the Harlot' as some of their best, loving their raw power and punk-like production values. Iron Maiden's reputation is based on a series of 80s albums of which *Beast* was the first, followed by *Peace of Mind* (1983), *Powerslave* (1984), *Somewhere In Time* (1986) and *Seventh Son of a Seventh Son* (1988). After an ill fated change of singer, Dickinson returned and there was a resurgence in their popularity in 2006 with the release of *A Matter of Life and Death* which brought them a whole new generation of fans.

The Number Of The Beast

Iron Maiden

Words & Music by Steve Harris

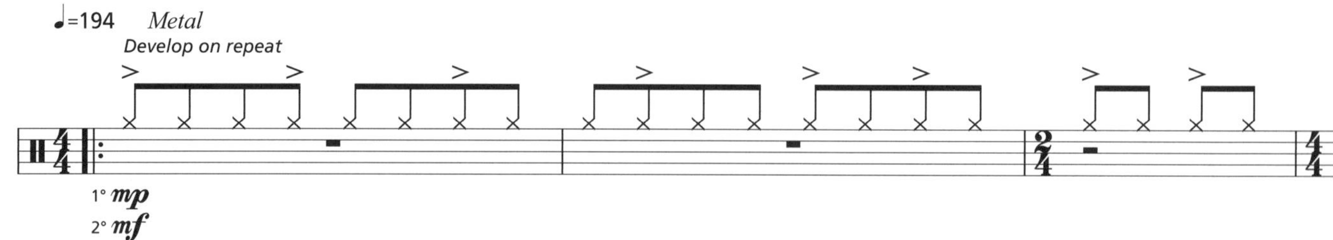

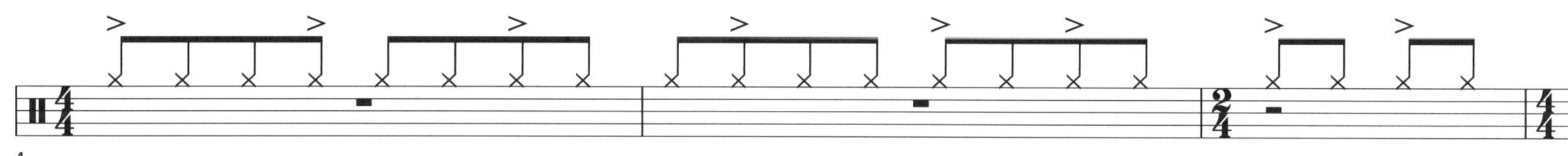

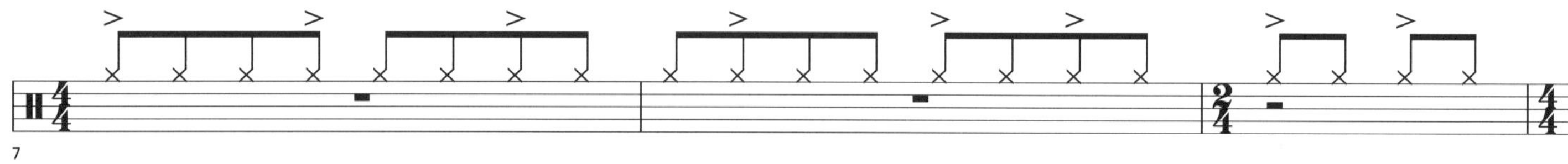

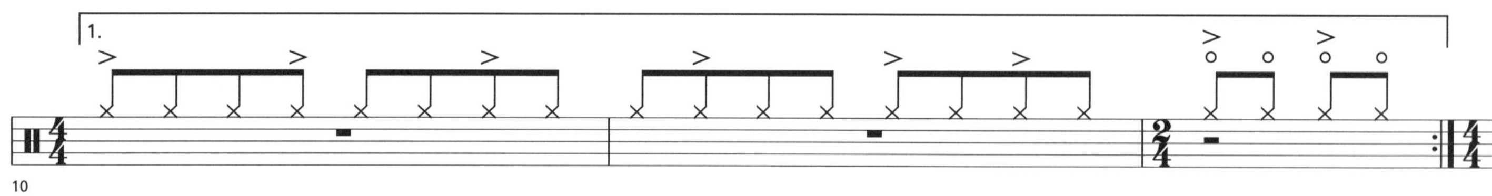

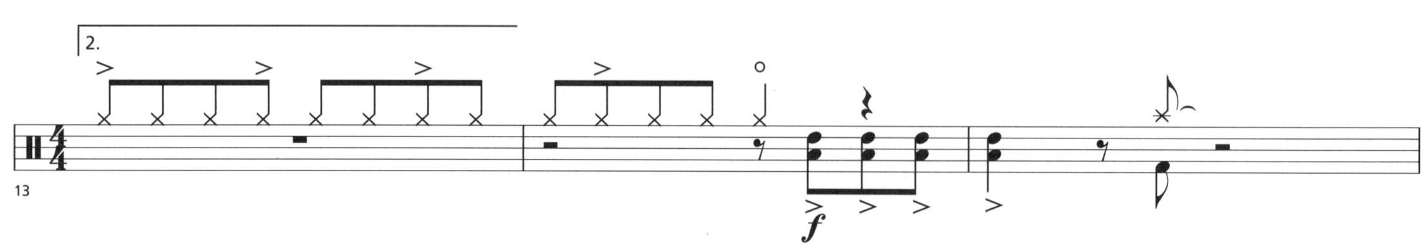

16

19

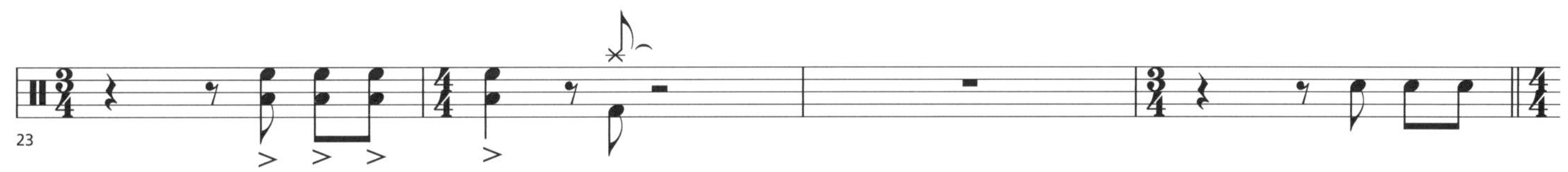
23

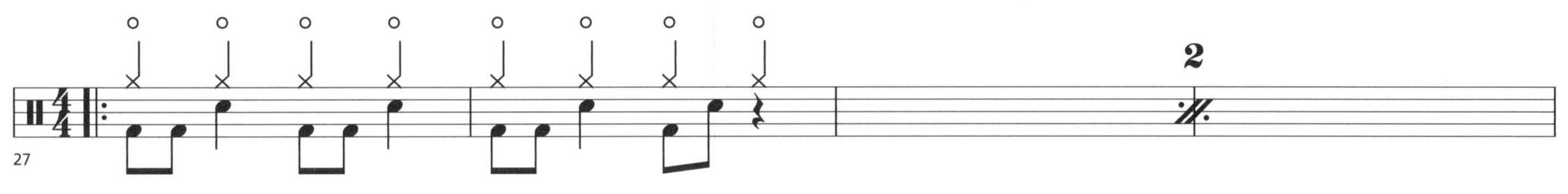
27
2

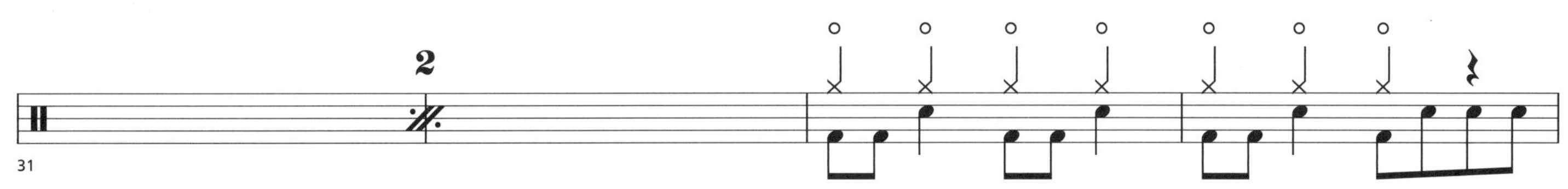
31
2

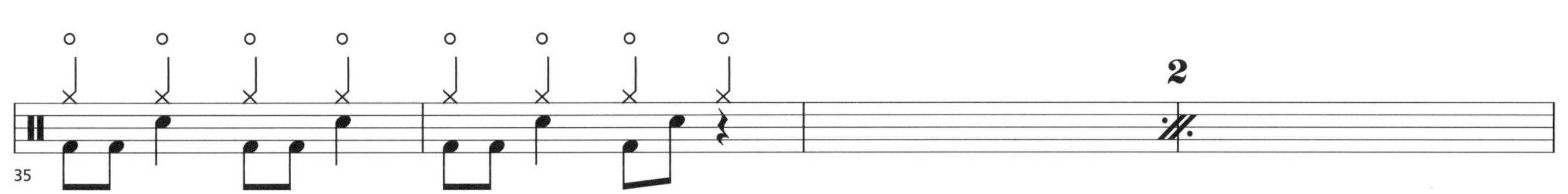
35
2

2
39
43
46
1.
2.
49
53
p
f
56
p

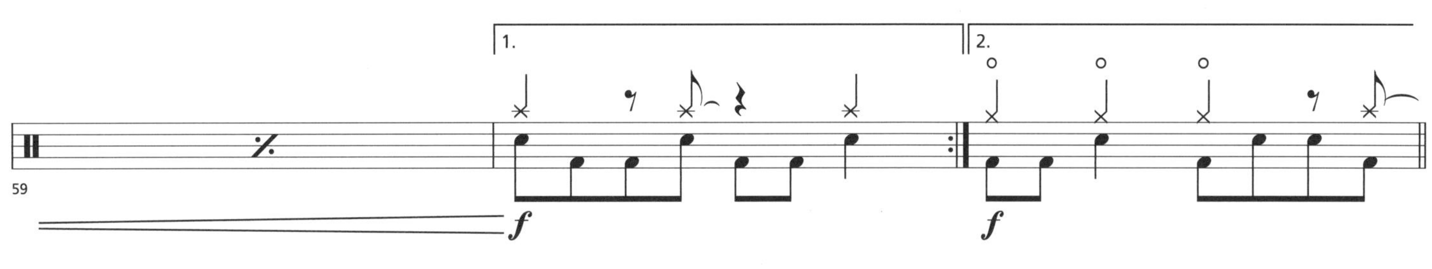
1.
2.
f
f

cont. sim.

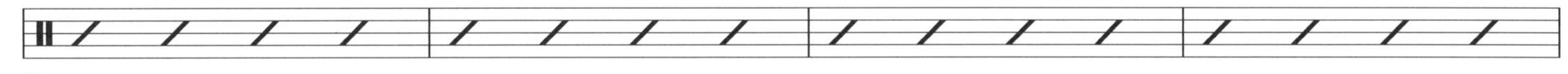

Fill
Fill

Walkthrough

Intro (Bars 1–26)

The first part of the intro includes some unorthodox accents on the hi-hat and the second part features challenging rock accents around the kit. The main challenge here is the changing time signature and maintaining a steady pulse.

Bars 1–3 | *Hi hat phrase*

This phrase follows the guitar line. Mathematically, we are combining the eighth notes of two 4/4 bars and one 2/4 bar (20 in total) and dividing them using the following accent pattern: 3, 3, 3, 3, 2, 2, 2, 2. The accent will be placed on the first stroke of every group. If you find yourself struggling, try listening to the guitar line and sing the rhythms in order to internalise the phrase. Remember that the dynamic level here is moderately quiet. On the repeat you should develop the part to show your stylistic understanding.

Bars 15–17 | *4/4 vs. 3/4*

This challenging phrase is being played over two 4/4 bars and one 3/4 bar (11 quarter beats in total). The key is counting all the beats, listening to the click on the backing track and remembering to change the counting to 3 in the 3/4 bar. Practising each bar separately with a metronome while counting the beats out loud is the best way to prepare.

Verse (Bars 27–42)

This is the first time the full groove comes in. The repetitive pattern allows you to focus on maintaining a steady pulse.

Bars 27–28 | *Verse Groove*

Technically, this groove is not too demanding. However, the displaced snare in bar 28, which is played on the offbeat of the third beat (an eighth note earlier than most common backbeats) may prove to be a challenge. Focus on the pulse and listen to the other instruments on the backing track while playing.

Chorus (Bars 43–52)

The groove changes in this section and some syncopated crashes over the bar line are added.

Bars 43–44 | *Syncopated & tied notes*

The eighth-note crash at the end of bar 43 feels unexpected, as it emphasises the weaker part of the bar: the offbeat. This is called 'syncopation'. In addition, this crash note is connected with a tie to the next crash note. This indicates that you do not have to play the second note, however the rhythmic value of the note must be preserved in order to maintain the pulse and sync. Listening to the bass guitar pattern in this section will be helpful (see Fig. 1).

Bars 43–44 | *Snare velocities*

Notice the two consecutive eighth notes on the snare. If both are played with the left hand, there is a danger that the velocity will not be balanced. If both are played with alternate sticking this may lead to inconsistent pulse.

C part (Bars 53–61)

This section combines a straightforward rock beat with the classic 3:3:2 accents. Playing it accurately with the constant dynamic changes will require a fair amount of practise.

Bar 56 | *3:3:2*

This refers to accenting the first note in each group of eight eighth notes that are divided to 3, 3, and 2. In this example both hands play the accent and the kick drum fills in between. This rhythmic phrase will be very useful as it can be used in many styles.

Guitar solo (Bars 62–81)

In this section you have the opportunity to vary the written patterns as well as adding your personal touch when improvising fills.

Bars 78–79 | *Improvised fill*

You have six beats to improvise on before the notated fill in the middle of bar 79. The guitar will be playing a line during these beats, so you can decide to follow it or play something around it. Ensure that the pulse is clear throughout your improvisation and whatever you are trying to execute sounds convincing (see Fig. 2).

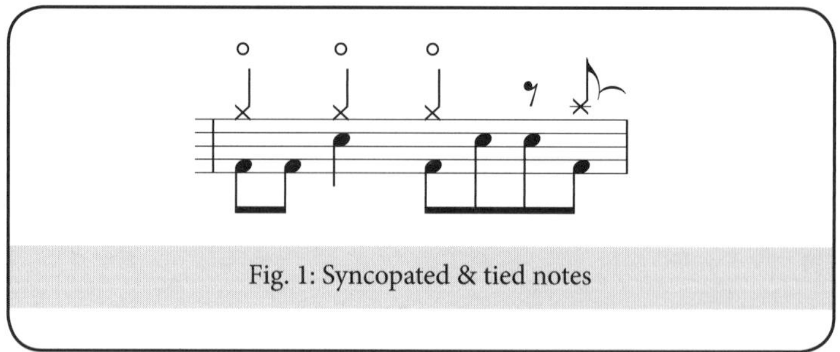

Fig. 1: Syncopated & tied notes

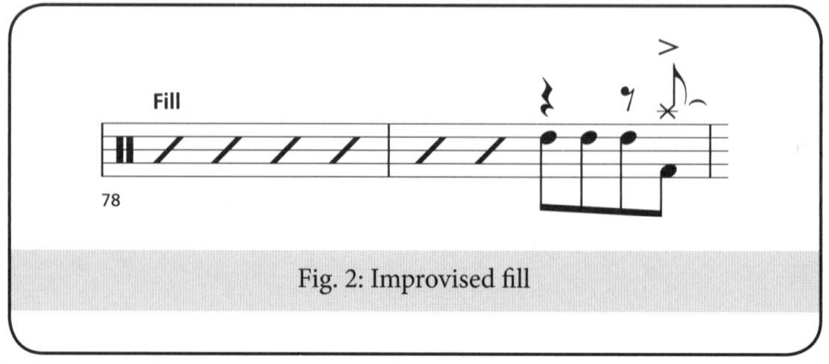

Fig. 2: Improvised fill

Red Hot Chili Peppers

SONG TITLE: THE ZEPHYR SONG
ALBUM: BY THE WAY
RELEASED: 2002
LABEL: WARNER BROTHERS
GENRE: ALTERNATIVE ROCK

PERSONNEL: ANTHONY KIEDIS (VOX)
JOHN FRUSCIANTE (GTR)
FLEA (BASS)
CHAD SMITH (DRUMS)

UK CHART PEAK: 11
US CHART PEAK: 49

BACKGROUND INFO

'The Zephyr Song' is the second single from the 2002 release *By The Way*. An uplifting, rather dreamy, love song, it features the supple playing of long-serving drummer Chad Smith. The laid-back feel of this groove belies the control needed to make it work. Here it's a case of less being definitely more, with subtle interplay between the snare drum and kick drum beats.

THE BIGGER PICTURE

The Chili Peppers have been releasing albums for nearly 30 years but have worked with legendary producer Rick Rubin for most of the last twenty. Known for his 'hands off' approach, where he allows the bands he works with space to breathe without imposing his personal style on them, the Rubin/Chili Peppers partnership saw the band break through with *Blood Sugar Sex Magic* (1991) and rise to mega-stardom courtesy of four more highly regarded albums. Guitarist John Frusciante left the band for the 1995 album *One Hot Minute*. The album was relatively unsuccessful, but Frusciante's return in time for 1999's *Californication* saw the band return to their funk rock roots, a moved that received both critical acclaim and even greater commercial success.

NOTES

Chad Smith is also known for moonlighting in so-called super group Chickenfoot, alongside Joe Satriani and Van Halen stalwarts Sammy Hagar and Michael Anthony. Their first album is due to be released in 2011. His other side project, Chad Smith's Bombastic Meatbeats, was formed as a backing band for former Deep Purple bassist Glenn Hughes, but has since continued with a life of its own, releasing three albums.

RECOMMENDED LISTENING

Chad Smith and Michael Balzary ('Flea') make a most impressive rhythm section by anyone's standards. Chad Smith cites as his influences the major rock drummers of the 60s and 70s: John Bonham, Bill Ward, Ginger Baker and Mitch Mitchell. His Bonham influences can certainly be heard on tracks such as 'Blood Sugar Sex Magic' and 'Breaking the Girl' (both off *Blood Sugar Sex Magic*), but equally his funk chops are fully to the fore in songs like 'Torture Me' and perennial favourite 'Hump de Bump', (both from *Stadium Arcadium*, 2006). These two songs are a throwback to the band's earlier funk roots and which can be heard on Chili Peppers' albums such as *The Uplift Mofo Party* (1987).

The Zephyr Song

Red Hot Chili Peppers

Words & Music by Anthony Kiedis, Flea, John Frusciante & Chad Smith

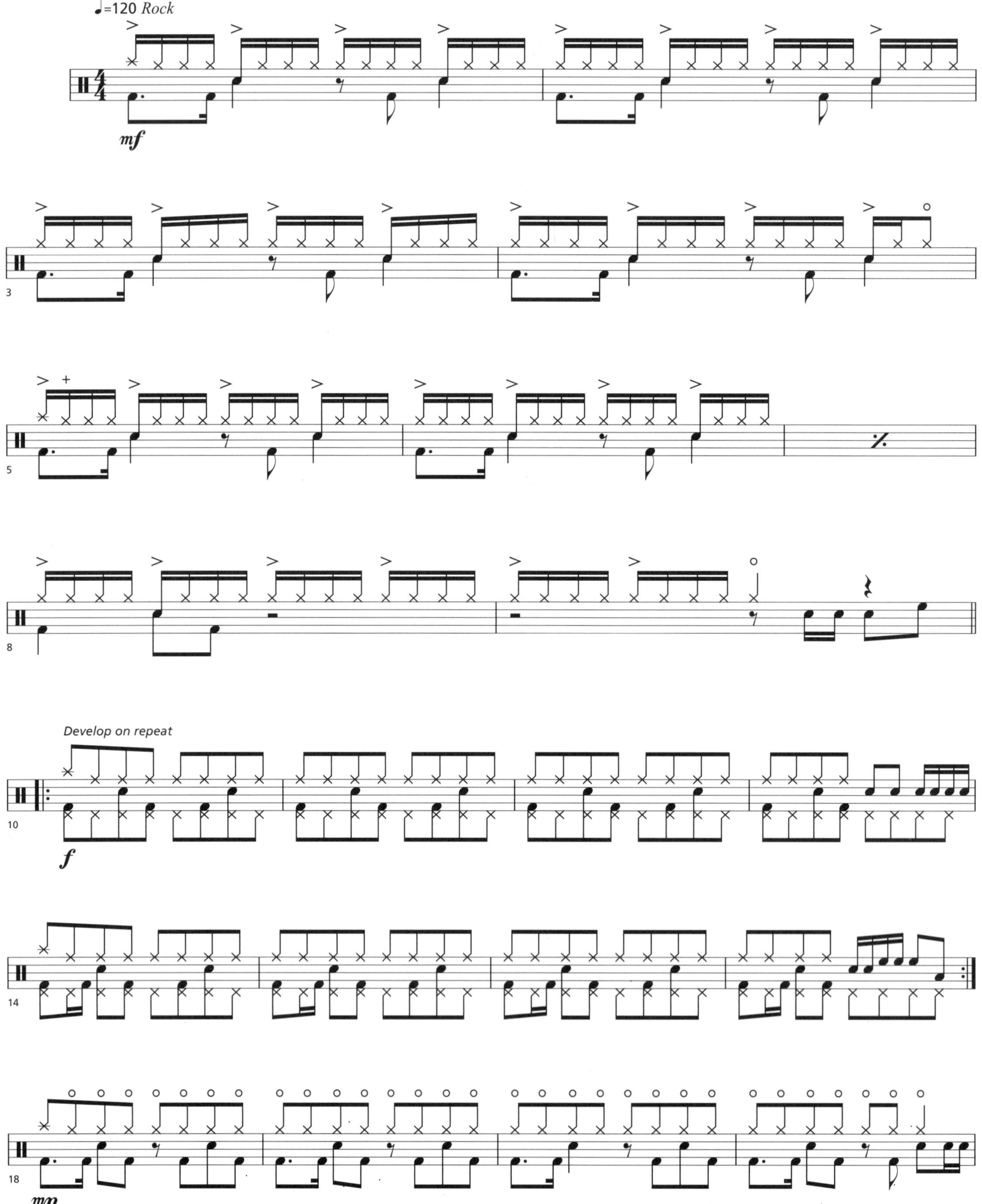

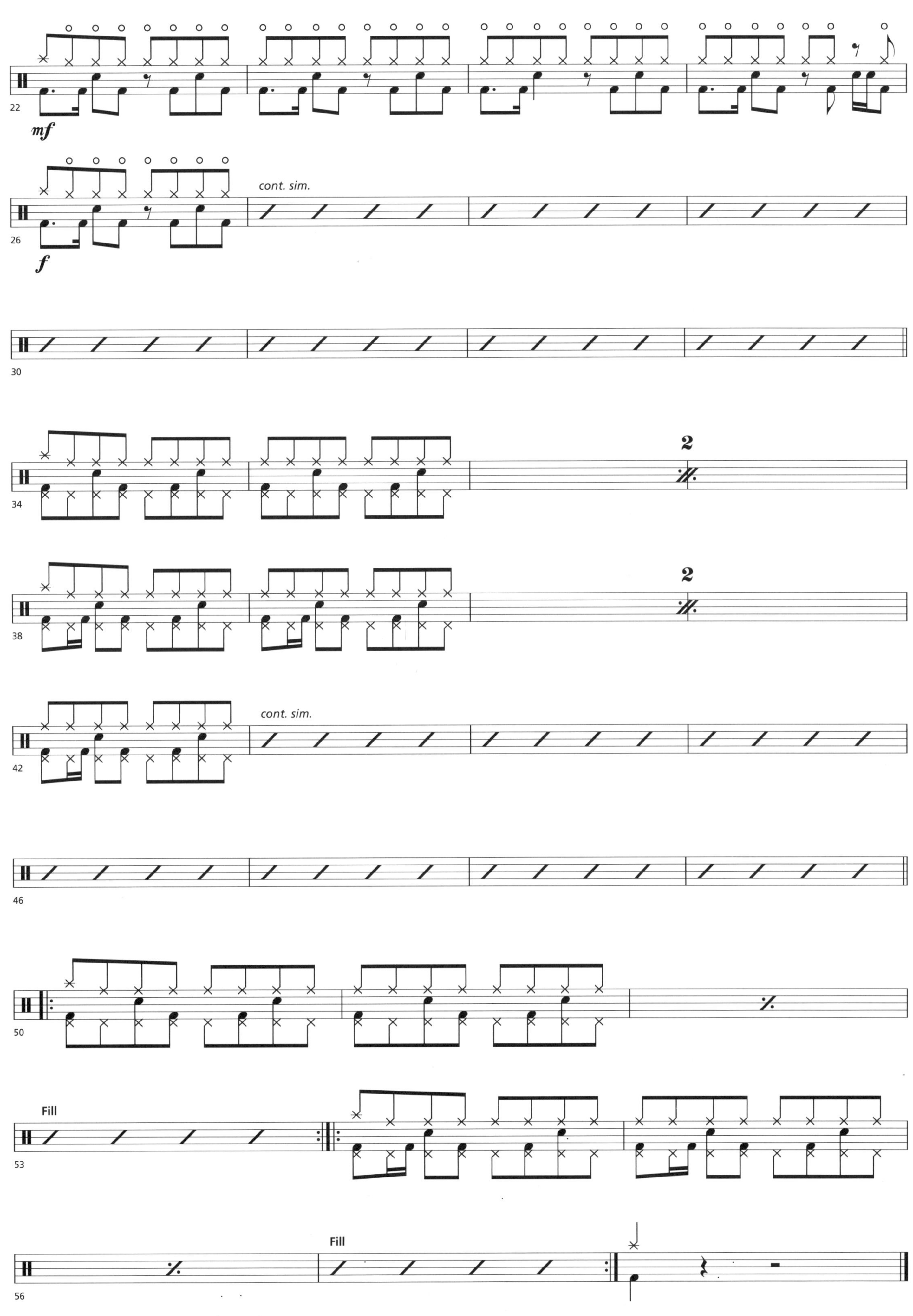
mf
f
cont. sim.
2
2
cont. sim.
Fill
Fill

Walkthrough

Verse (Bars 1–9)

This examined part starts from the second verse of the original song. The groove consists of sixteenth notes on the hi-hat with some funky kick drums and, of course, the backbeat snare.

Bar 1 | *Verse groove*
This type of sixteenth-note hi-hat beat is played with alternate sticking. The right hand should move from the hi-hat to the snare in order to play the backbeat then immediately return to the hi-hat. Ensure that all hi-hats are even, the backbeat is consistent and the accents are performed in sync. Coordinating the sixteenth-note kick drum with the hands pattern can be challenging, therefore invest some time solving any coordination difficulties prior to playing the full groove. Naturally, the most difficult part of this groove is the sixteenth-note kick drum that is played with the hi-hat left hand (the weaker hand).

Bar 4 | *Open hi-hat*
The right hand should play the open hi-hat stroke and you will need to time this well in order to achieve the required open sound. It is very important to notice that the hi-hat should not be closed immediately, but remain open until the closed hi-hat notation appears in the following bar.

Chorus (Bars 10–17)

The chorus groove is based on the ride cymbal with the addition of a hi-hat foot pattern. On the repeat you have the opportunity to develop the part and show your stylistic understanding and musicality.

Bar 10 | *Chorus groove*
Reliable four-way coordination will be required in order to perform this groove well. The hi-hat foot will most commonly be played with the heel up technique in order to achieve the stylistic sound. Start with the hi-hat foot and add the ride cymbal (which plays the same pattern). Then, add the backbeat snare and when you feel ready add the kick drum pattern. Take your time and practise this beat at various speeds and dynamic levels. Including hi-hat foot patterns in beats will add a whole new dimension to your drumming (see Fig. 1).

Guitar solo & Bridge (Bars 18–33)

The groove changes again in this section and there are many important dynamic details. From bar 27 the instruction *cont. sim.* implies that variations to the groove should be made. Remember that these must be musical, stylistic and tightly in sync.

Bar 18 | *Open hi-hat groove*
Releasing the left foot grip from the hi-hat pedal will create the open hi-hat sound. In order to keep it consistent, ensure that you are comfortable and your foot remains in the same position throughout the groove.

The hectic kick drum pattern needs to be accurate so attention should be paid to the sixteenth-note kick drums. The dynamic level in this bar is moderately quiet, this can be naturally created by keeping the sticks (and kick drum beater) close to the drum heads (see Fig. 2).

Second chorus (Bars 34–49)

The groove is identical to the first chorus and your stamina and consistent sound projection will be tested here. Bars 34–42 should be played as written, however from bar 43 you are expected to add stylistic variations to the part. These can be added kick drums, added sixteenth notes on the snare drum, crash hits or short fills.

Outro (Bars 50–end)

Although the groove remains the same throughout the outro section, you have the opportunity to add your individual improvised fills. Listen to the full version of this track and similar Red Hot Chili Peppers songs for improvisation ideas and inspiration.

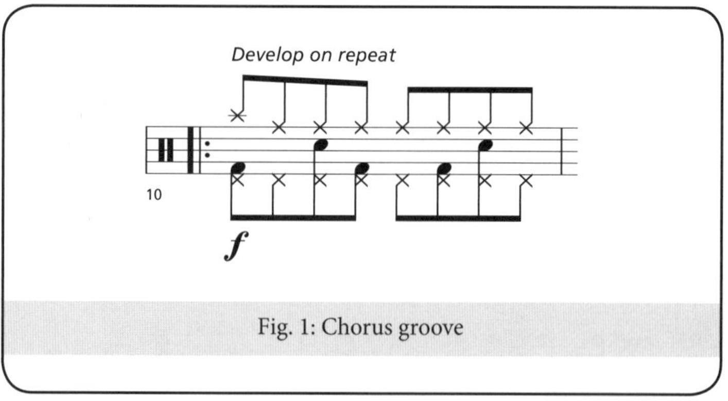

Fig. 1: Chorus groove

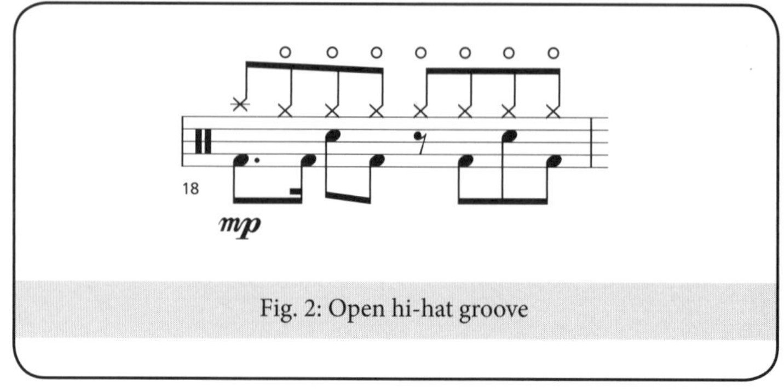

Fig. 2: Open hi-hat groove

DRUM NOTATION EXPLAINED

BASS DRUM & TOMS

Bass drum | Floor tom | Medium tom | High tom

SNARE

Snare | Ghost snare | Rim-shot | Cross stick | Buzz snare

Rim-shot: *Strike snare drum and surrounding rim at same time*

Cross stick: *Place palm on snare drum head and strike rim with stick*

HI-HAT

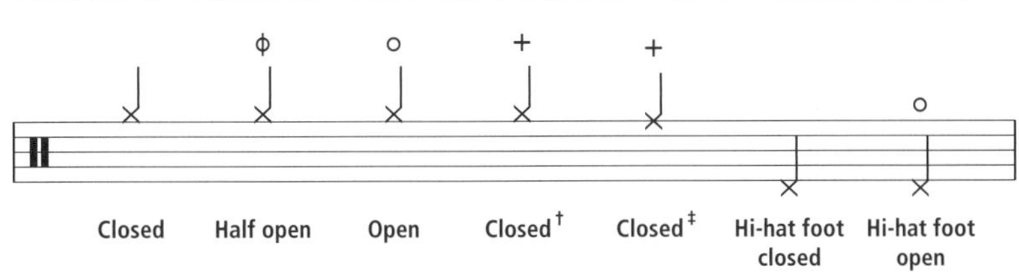

Closed | Half open | Open | Closed † | Closed ‡ | Hi-hat foot closed | Hi-hat foot open

† Used on the first closed hi-hat that follows an open hi-hat

‡ The hi-hat is closed without being struck. Note that the hi-hat closed (cross) symbol may appear above drum voices other than the hi-hat (as shown above). This simply means another drum voice is being played at the same moment that the hi-hat is being closed.

OTHER CYMBALS

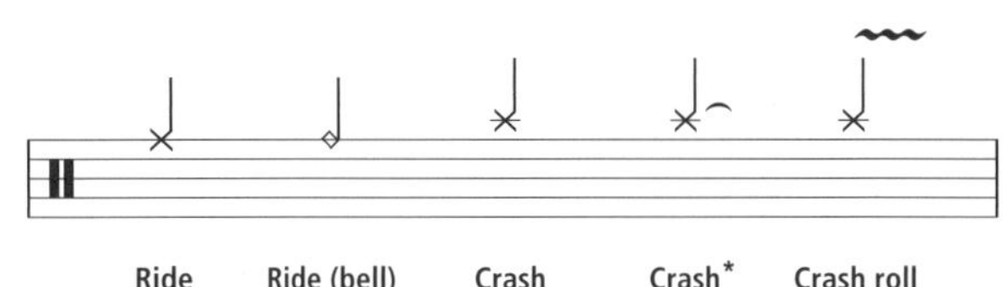

Ride | Ride (bell) | Crash | Crash * | Crash roll

__Allow all cymbals to ring on__ unless explicitly stopped, as indicated by the keyword __'Choke'__. Occasionally ties may be used (*) to emphasise that cymbals should be allowed to ring on. This can avoid confusion during syncopations and pushes.

GENERAL MUSIC NOTATION

Accentuate note (play it louder).

Slashes are used to demarcate bars during solos, fills, developments and other ad lib. sections.

D.𝄋. al Coda

Go back to the sign (𝄋) then play until the bar marked ***To Coda*** 𝄌 then skip to the section marked 𝄌 ***Coda***.

Repeat the bars between the repeat signs.

D.C. al Fine

Go back to beginning of song and play until bar marked ***Fine*** (end).

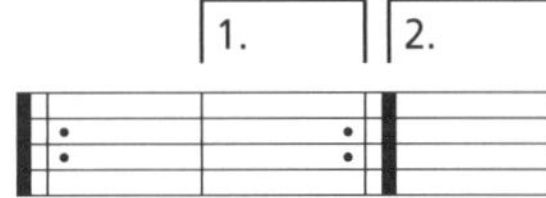

When a repeated section has different endings, play the first ending only the first time and the second ending only the second time.

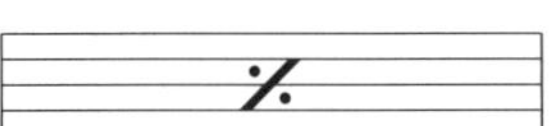

Repeat the previous bar. In higher grades these may also be marked *sim.* or *cont. sim.*

Repeat the previous two bars. In higher grades these may also be marked *sim.* or *cont. sim.*

In rudiments, each stem slash subdivides the note value by half.

MUSICAL TERMS WITH SPECIFIC EXAMINATION DEFINITIONS

Fill	Play an individual, stylistic fill.
Cont. sim.	Continue in similar way but vary the pattern slightly.
Develop	Extend the musical part in a stylistically appropriate manner.
Rit. (ritardando)	Gradually slow the tempo.

Free Choice Pieces, Entering Exams and Marking schemes

Free Choice Pieces

The songs featured in Hot Rock are arranged for use as free choice pieces in Rockschool exams. In the grade exams you can play up to two tracks from this book alongside one choice from the Rockschool Grade 5 book. If you are taking the Performance Certificate exam you may play up to three tracks from this book alongside two choices from the Rockschool Grade 5 book.

Entering Exams

Entering a Rockschool exam is easy. You may enter online at *www.rockschool.co.uk* or by downloading and filling in an exam entry form. The full Rockschool examination terms and conditions as well as exam periods and current fees are available from our website or by calling +44 (0)845 460 4747.

Marking Schemes

Below are the marking schemes for the two different types of Rockschool exam.

Grade Exams | Grades 1–5

ELEMENT	PASS	MERIT	DISTINCTION
Performance Piece 1	12–14 out of 20	15–17 out of 20	18+ out of 20
Performance Piece 2	12–14 out of 20	15–17 out of 20	18+ out of 20
Performance Piece 3	12–14 out of 20	15–17 out of 20	18+ out of 20
Technical Exercises	9–10 out of 15	11–12 out of 15	13+ out of 15
Either Sight Reading *or* Improvisation & Interpretation	6 out of 10	7–8 out of 10	9+ out of 10
Ear Tests	6 out of 10	7–8 out of 10	9+ out of 10
General Musicianship Questions	3 out of 5	4 out of 5	5 out of 5
TOTAL MARKS	**60%+**	**74%+**	**90%+**

Performance Certificates | Grades 1–8

ELEMENT	PASS	MERIT	DISTINCTION
Performance Piece 1	12–14 out of 20	15–17 out of 20	18+ out of 20
Performance Piece 2	12–14 out of 20	15–17 out of 20	18+ out of 20
Performance Piece 3	12–14 out of 20	15–17 out of 20	18+ out of 20
Performance Piece 4	12–14 out of 20	15–17 out of 20	18+ out of 20
Performance Piece 5	12–14 out of 20	15–17 out of 20	18+ out of 20
TOTAL MARKS	**60%+**	**75%+**	**90%+**

Copyright Information

Audio Copyright

Cherub Rock
(Corgan)
Universal/MCA Music Limited.

Chop Suey!
(Tankian/Malakian)
DDevil Music/Sony/ATV Tunes LLC.

Hey Joe
(Roberts)
Carlin Music Corporation.

Late In The Evening
(Simon)
Copyright Control

Master Of Puppets
(Hetfield/Ulrich/Burton/Hammett)
Universal Music Publishing Limited.

My Generation
(Townshend)
Fabulous Music Limited.

The Number Of The Beast
(Harris)
Imagem Music.

The Zephyr Song
(Kiedis/Flea/Frusciante/Smith)
Moebetoblame Music.

mcps

Photographic Rights

Jimmy Chamberlin – The Smashing Pumpkins
Page 5
© Jeffrey Bender/Corbis

John Dolmayan – System Of A Down
Page 11
© Tim Mosenfelder/Corbis

Mitch Mitchell – The Jimi Hendrix Experience
Page 17
Hoepla/1967
© CC BY-SA 3.0 NL License

Steve Gadd – Paul Simon
Page 21
roberto scorta
flickr.com/photos/rosco57
© CC BY 2.0 License

Lars Ulrich – Metallica
Page 25
© Jeff Gerew/Corbis

Keith Moon – The Who
Page 31
Bill Abbott
flickr.com/photos/wbaiv
© CC BY-SA 2.0 License

Clive Burr – Iron Maiden
Page 37
© Lipo Musto/REX

Chad Smith – Red Hot Chili Peppers
Page 43
Kristy Fox
flickr.com/photos/kristyfox
© CC BY 2.0 License

Use of Creative Commons licensed material based on the information provided by the assumed rights holder. Detailed license information is available from http://creativecommons.org/licenses.

Our practical diplomas are the next step for any Grade 8 musician wanting to start a career in teaching or performance

Music Teaching Diploma
Level 4

Music Teaching Licentiate
Level 6

Teaching Diplomas
are for self-employed teachers who want to develop their skills, or musicians who want to go into music education

Music Performance Diploma
Level 4

Music Performance Licentiate
Level 6

Performance Diplomas
are for artists who wish to develop their existing performance skills and learn about the business and marketing side to being an independent artist

VOCATIONAL QUALIFICATIONS

Our vocational qualifications offer practical structured learning with the flexibility to specialise in different areas of the music industry.

Available at Levels 1–4. Vocational Qualifications are a real alternative to GCSE, A-Level and BTECs.

Music Practitioners
opens the door to all aspects of the music industry from composition and performance to business and technology

Creative Practitioners
provides structured support for artists wanting to develop themselves and get started in the industry

LET'S
ROCK
START PLAYING NOW!

LET'S ROCK
START PLAYING NOW!
DRUMS
BASS
GUITAR
Includes over 1 HOUR of downloadable audio & video material
Great for beginners
Extra tuition & quizzes

THE BASS
A QUICK GUIDE
All you need to know about this amazing instrument
DID YOU KNOW?